An Uneasy Dwelling

The story of the Philadelphia Association community houses

Paul Gordon

PCCS Books
Ross-on-Wye

First published in 2010

PCCS BOOKS Ltd
2 Cropper Row
Alton Road
Ross-on-Wye
Herefordshire
HR9 5LA
UK
Tel +44 (0)1989 763900
www.pccs-books.co.uk

© Paul Gordon, 2010

**An Uneasy Dwelling: The story of the Philadelphia association
community houses**

A CIP catalogue record for this book is available from the British Library

ISBN 978 1 906254 24 7

Cover image: 'Composition' Ossip Zadkine. By kind permission of the
Ossip Zadkine Foundation, Wiegersma Fine Art, Brussels, www.zadkine.com
Cover design by Old Dog Graphics
Printed by ImprintDigital.net, Exeter, UK

For my mother, Wilma, with love

And is this room really a room or an embrace
And what is beneath the window, a street or years?
And the window is only the imprint left by
The first rain we understood, returning endlessly.

And this wall does not define the room … .

Ivan Lalic, from *Places We Love* (trans. Charles Simic)

Contents

Acknowledgements

This book could not have been written without the help of several friends and colleagues. I am grateful to my fellow Philadelphia Association house therapists – Hilary Cooper, Ian McMillan and Jake Osborne – for our regular conversations over the years about the houses and for their thoughts about this account. I am grateful too to Martine Allouf, Helen Dunford, Mark Elmer and Christina Moutsou for their careful reading of the text and their constructive criticism and encouragement. Thanks also to Helen Spandler whose book, *Asylum to Action*, on the Paddington Day Hospital therapeutic community, inspired me to tell our story, and to Gareth Evans for the lines by Ivan Lalic which appear as an epigraph. Once again I am indebted to Pete Sanders and Maggie Taylor-Sanders of PCCS Books for their enthusiasm for this project and their care in its production. Hannah and Sarah Benn Gordon helped with the word-processing. They and Melissa Benn were the lively and loving community which allowed this book to take shape.

Paul Gordon
London
July 2010

Author's Notes

1. Chapter 3, 'The story of a house: Portland Road' is drawn from Robin Cooper's unpublished PhD thesis, 'Dwelling and Hospitality: A phenomenological inquiry into therapeutic community', and is included by kind permission of Hilary Cooper.

2. The names of all residents have been changed to protect their anonimity.

3. Any unsourced references are to papers in the Philadelphia Association's files, by kind permission of the PA.

Introduction

Providing places of asylum has been at the heart of the Philadelphia Association's endeavours for more than 40 years. Hundreds of men and women, whether formally designated 'mentally ill', or experiencing serious emotional distress to the point where they can no longer cope, have found in our houses a haven, a place where, in the company of others, they are allowed to go through whatever they have to go through, in their own time and in their own way, free from the well-meaning interventions of psychiatry or family. The most famous of these was undoubtedly the first, Kingsley Hall, which opened in 1965 and which has come to have an almost iconic status in the world of what has come to be called critical (or less accurately anti-) psychiatry.

When Kingsley Hall closed in 1970 (when the lease expired) the PA's attempt at providing a radically different approach to the treatment of those in states of severe emotional distress did not come to an end, as many people seem to believe. Rather it took different forms and has continued to this day. The weekend that the PA moved out of Kingsley Hall, a new community opened and more than 15 houses have been run under our auspices since and several hundred people have spent some time in them. The houses have been an inspiration to many others too.

Despite our longevity and the radically different nature of our project, surprisingly little has been written about our work in this respect, a few book chapters and articles, and an unpublished PhD thesis. The Philadelphia Association (PA) has never been good at self-promotion. In part this was an

1

understandable reaction to the period when the PA was most closely identified with one of its founders, the highly public figure of RD Laing, but it has meant that what we do – which is arguably unique in its field – has felt at times like a guilty secret.

This book is an attempt to correct that. It is in part a history of the houses but I have not tried to produce a detailed factual account of who did what, and what happened when and where. This would be of doubtful interest even to ourselves, let alone others outside the PA network. It would also be of questionable accuracy as we move further and further away from the events themselves and when, sadly, many of the important actors in the drama – RD Laing, David Cooper, Hugh Crawford, Aaron Esterson, Robin Cooper and Sid Briskin – are no longer with us. In any case, like many radical organisations of its time, the PA kept very little indeed in the way of documentation of its activities and there is very little in the way of primary sources from which to work. The PA was, quite rightly, more concerned with just getting on and actually doing things, or at least trying to, than with recording its deliberations. (The existing files on the PA communities in the first 20 years *together* take up half the space of the files of *one* of the current houses.)

The history presented here is in part a means to an end, it's a way of making sense of how we have come to be here and why we work in the ways that we do. In the end this is a book about our houses *now*, what we do and why. How did we get here and how do we account for ourselves? What is it that we do and does it matter? How are we different from others who may seem similar and why? These are some of the questions I have tried to pose.

This is obviously not a disinterested account. I, and the colleagues who have helped me write this, have been involved in these houses for a long time. I believe in them and what they do, a belief that comes from my experience, and that of my colleagues: present and in the past. In that context, this is also a celebration of an achievement.

Nevertheless I do not claim to speak for others, let alone for the Philadelphia Association as a whole. In the end this is *my* account, and the decisions about what to include and the emphases and interpretations of the account, are my responsibility, as are any errors of fact. That said, I do hope this book speaks to, and of, the experiences of others.

CHAPTER 1

Kingsley Hall
'Something was shown there'

In the summer of 1965 a group of people, who had for a long time been concerned at the definition and treatment of the 'mentally ill', took over a large community settlement building in Bow, east London. The grim location, in London's deprived and run-down east end, seemed an unlikely setting perhaps for what they had in mind, which was nothing less than the creation of a true alternative to the mental hospitals of the day. The plan was to provide a haven, a place of genuine asylum, where those in extreme mental distress might go through whatever they were going through free from medical intervention, whether in the form of heavy drugs or insulin comas or electric shock treatment, or even lobotomies, which were at the time the main 'treatments' in many hospitals for those designated 'mentally ill'. The building was called Kingsley Hall and the name was to enter the lexicon of discussions about mental distress and its treatment, whether as a shorthand for all that was wrong with the alleged anarchy and permissiveness of the times, or as shorthand for a new (usually highly idealised) way of helping those suffering.

Those who took over the building, calling themselves the Philadelphia Association, had been looking for some time for a suitable place where they might try to put their ideas into practice. The radical psychiatrist and psychoanalyst, RD Laing, for instance, who himself moved into the library of Kingsley Hall in June, had most recently been involved with a group of parents in the St John's Wood area of north London, some of whose sons and daughters had experienced breakdowns and who were looking to set up a kind of crisis centre as an alternative to hospital. The plans, like so many at the time, came to nothing for lack of funding, but it was this 'Philadelphia Project', drawing its name from the Greek for brotherly – and by contemporary extension sisterly – love, which gave Laing the name for the new enterprise. Others involved in the new project included the psychiatrists David Cooper and Aaron Esterson, the radical writer Clancy Sigal, Joan Cunnold, a former psychiatric nurse, and Sid Briskin, a colleague of Laing and Esterson who had worked with them on their research into families.

These people hoped to create a place of asylum in its true sense of the word, a place of refuge or sanctuary, deriving from the Greek from inviolable or safe from violence. (Its modern usage of a place for those designated 'mentally ill' is comparatively recent, the late 18th century. Even then the asylum was still a place of refuge.) Laing said later:

> It is very confusing if a place of hospitality (a hospital) is a prison – even a special prison – but a prison not a haven, an asylum, a refuge, a check-out place, a sanctuary. You come there and the doors are locked. You're not allowed to go out … The most important thing in an environment, as far as safety goes, is the people in it. So we try to experiment with how *we* can, in our context, be safe for other people to meet. When we don't know people, people we've never met before, we have to show by our presence that we are not going to do anything to anyone in the name of anything. (Evans, 1976: 89–90)

Kingsley Hall itself was a community settlement which had been set up in the 1920s by the philanthropists Doris and Muriel Lester to serve the poor of the locality. Named in memory of their dead brother, Kingsley, it was associated with many radical causes including the Suffragettes. Mahatma Gandhi had stayed there (with his goat) in 1931 when he came to London to negotiate British withdrawal from India. But by the early 1960s the building had been vacant for some time and its trustees were keen to see it in use once more. In many ways, it was ideal for what the new Philadelphia Association had in mind; it stood on its own ground, unattached to any other buildings, and it was large, with substantial communal areas and several small spaces that could be used as bedrooms. Laing had heard about the building from Sid Briskin, who had worked with him and Esterson on their research into families of people diagnosed 'schizophrenic', and had several meetings with Muriel Lester to put his case about what he called the 'serious gross violation of primitive human decency' that went on in mental hospitals. Lester, Laing said, was unfamiliar with the issues but was sympathetic and the trustees agreed to lend the building to the new group at a notional rent for five years from 1965 until 1970 (Mullan,1995: 175).

A different response

Laing and others had believed for a long time that a different way of responding to mental distress was not only necessary but possible. As a young psychiatrist at Glasgow's Gartnavel Royal Mental Hospital in the early 1950s he had been assigned to the female refractory ward, a place where the long-stay patients, some of whom had been there for many years, reminded him of the ghosts in Homer's descriptions of Hades: the patients 'lived across Rivers of Fear'. Laing recalled how he would spend a few hours in the day room every day over a period of several months. It was clear, he said, that the patients, usually thought of as autistic and completely withdrawn into themselves, were in reality desperate for human contact. Laing was given permission by the hospital superintendent, Dr Angus MacNiven and the matron, to try out an experiment in the management of a few of these chronic patients. Eleven patients and two nurses were given a room to themselves from 9am until 5pm, Mondays to Fridays. All those selected were people who had been diagnosed schizophrenic and who had been on the ward for at least four years. On the first day, Laing recalled, the patients had to be shepherded from the ward into the day-room. On the second day, at 8.30, they were all clustered around the locked door waiting to get in. It was, Laing said, 'one of the most moving experiences of my life'. Within 18 months, all 11 patients were able to leave hospital. Within one year, however, they were all back. 'Had they found more companionship "inside" than they could find "outside"?' Laing asked (Laing, 1985).

A few years later, David Cooper, a young South African psychiatrist, took up a post at the huge (2,000 beds) mental hospital at Shenley, north-west of London. Cooper was assigned to one of the 'villas' into which the hospital was organised. Villa 21 had been an insulin coma ward and was now free. Like Laing, Cooper was to be allowed to run an experiment, this time in the treatment of young men diagnosed as schizophrenic. Villa 21 had 19 beds and common rooms. The patients were men in their teens through to their late 20s. Most had been diagnosed as schizophrenic, the others with personality disorder or adolescent emotional crisis. All patients were discharged from hospital within one year of admission. The 'experiment' is described in some detail in Cooper's book *Psychiatry and Anti-Psychiatry*, published in 1967. Here let us just note that what Cooper and his colleagues aimed to do was provide what they called 'a human context' where the kinds of situations that led to psychotic behaviour were avoided as far as possible. 'Each patient was assured of a relationship with at least one other person significant to him. This relationship was as consistent and reliable as we could achieve.' To this end several 'social therapists' were trained in the year before the unit opened, people drawn from the nursing staff whose task would be to establish with patients a consistent relationship of trust. The focus in the unit shifted from the individual to the family and the milieu (Cooper, 1967).

Both Laing and Cooper in their accounts noted that one of the greatest obstacles to change of this kind was nothing to

changes of
burden of responsibility

do with what might be 'wrong' with the patients but a lot to do with those in traditional roles of psychiatrist or nurse who were unwilling to give up their authority and power.

A few years after the Gartnavel experiment, Laing and another Scottish psychiatrist, Aaron Esterson, began to study families, one of whose members had been diagnosed as 'schizophrenic', and published 11 of their studies in 1964 under the title, *Sanity, Madness and the Family: Families of schizophrenics*.[1] Laing and Esterson rejected the very idea of 'schizophrenia' as 'a biochemical, neurophysiological, [or] psychological' fact. Given the state of the evidence, this was 'palpable error', they said, They sought instead to see whether 'the experience and behaviour that psychiatrists take as symptoms and signs of schizophrenia [were] more socially intelligible than has come to be supposed?' Their conclusion was stark: 'if one looks, in the way we have, at the experience and behaviour of the person whose experience and behaviour are invalidated, they take on a complexion very different from that seen from the usual clinical psychiatric vantage points, or dis-vantage points' (Laing and Esterson,1964).

It was in this context that people tried to *do* something different from the standard response. In the United States the work of the psychiatrist and psychoanalyst Harry Stack Sullivan showed that episodes of psychotic breakdown could be dealt with in a matter of months given the right kind of environment, small, humane, and staffed by people able to relate in a non-destructive way to those in their care. In Britain there was the experience of the Richmond Fellowship, run by Elly Jansen, who believed that an attitude of open-mindedness and acceptance helped to make sense of psychosis and to maintain contact with the person going through the crisis. Laing knew Jansen and had visited one of the Richmond Fellowship 'half-way houses', places positioned between the hospital and

---

1. Esterson would look at one of these cases in much more detail in his own *The Leaves of Spring*, subtitled 'a study in the dialectics of madness' (Esterson, 1970).

independent living. They had even talked of working together, but Laing wanted something more radical, 'a whole-way house' (Mullan, 1995: 177).[2] And in 1963 Sid Briskin opened his own family home to several people, former residents of Villa 21, who had been diagnosed schizophrenic.[3] Laing himself, after his first marriage had ended and his family had returned to Glasgow, also gave his home in north London over to this purpose. Run first by Bill Mason, and later by the psychotherapist Ben Churchill, this stayed open for three years from May 1966 until August 1969. Some 75 people stayed in these two houses. (As was to happen so often with the PA houses, within a short time of opening, local officials were trying to designate the places as medical and to bring them under their control. The local Medical Officer of Health wrote to Laing saying there were a number of 'mentally-disordered people' at the house and this meant the house had to be registered as a residential home for such people. Laing replied: 'The house does not set out to be a therapeutic community', although he had heard it alluded to as such.)

Mary Barnes – and others

More than 100 people came to stay at Kingsley Hall during its short lifetime but the one resident people are likely to have heard of is Mary Barnes. With her therapist, Joe Berke, she embarked on a journey of regression, a journey later described by them in their joint book, *Mary Barnes: Two accounts of a journey through madness* (Barnes & Berke, 1971). (This would later be

2. Jansen wrote about her relationship with Laing in Mullan (ed.) 1997.
3. The highly unusual nature of this gesture, not to mention its generosity, can be gauged by Laing's story of how people diagnosed as schizophrenic were seen, at times by some, almost as though they had the plague or were simply dangerous. When cakes were offered round in a hospital doctors' sitting room, Laing once recalled, only two or three accepted, 'brave, or reckless, enough to eat a bun baked by a chronic schizophrenic'.)

adapted for the stage by the radical playwright, David Edgar.) In the book Barnes described her childhood and adolescence and her many breakdowns, her treatments in hospital including electro-shock treatment. She found her way to therapy with Laing's colleague, Aaron Esterson, and moved into Kingsley Hall soon after it opened. There, with her new therapist a young psychiatrist from the US called Joe Berke, she embarked on a journey of regression to an infantile state, being fed from a bottle, smearing her shit on the walls and on herself. Barnes herself would go on to become an artist, working until her death in 2001 (Barnes with Scott, 1989).

Barnes was only one of the many who went to Kingsley Hall and her regression was unique and never repeated at Kingsley Hall or elsewhere, but her story, especially the fantasy of a psychological or emotional rebirth, touched many. Indeed it continues to bring some people to the PA houses today.

Another young US psychiatrist who lived at Kingsley Hall for a year, Morton Schatzman, interviewed several residents during his stay. These interviews, incorporated into an essay, 'Madness and morals', (Schatzman, 1972) constitute a rare and invaluable account of life at Kingsley Hall as it was seen by those actually living there. Discussing Mary Barnes, Schatzman first remarked that not everyone at Kingsley Hall desired or needed to undergo 'an experiential drama of this magnitude'. Many simply wished to be free from 'the well-intentioned misguided harassment of their families or mental hospitals or both. They want to live in a haven where they can simply be'.

One resident spoke of always having been in a position of having to do as he or she was told and somehow coming to expect this: 'And then initially when I came here I seemed to be the one who was arranging things and making decisions – arranging things and taking quite an active part'. This person added that one of the best things about being at Kingsley Hall was not having to be right: 'Being here, anything goes – sort of, I think of a word – an "acceptance" of people as they are which I've never found anywhere else'.

Another said:

> ... here a number of divergent people come together to meet
> and to try to live out a life with one another where they can
> live out their differences – have rows, disagree intently; decide
> to do things in ways that will offend others – and still for
> those to be tolerated, and for people doing this to become
> aware of other people and their inter-effects upon one another.

Another resident said:

> ... here I find that many people question things with a greater
> honesty. People with obvious honesty question many things
> that one has been taking to be unconditionally true and valid
> ... I feel that this very situation which makes *retreat* from *social
> reality* – well, external reality – possible; in fact eventually,
> paradoxically, makes facing *reality in general almost unavoidable*.

How, Schatzman asked, were decisions made at Kingsley Hall,
agreements reached, and implemented? The community
answered these questions in different ways at different times.
Gatherings were most frequent around the table or wherever
people met to eat and issues might be brought up here. People
sometimes agreed to meet at regular intervals, at set times, just
to share what they had on their minds, 'but can a genuine
meeting be scheduled?' it was asked. New residents would have
to meet some or all of the existing residents and would usually
be invited to stay for dinner or over a weekend. The community
invited to join those whom they liked or those whom they felt
would benefit from living there. It tried to strike a balance
between those who were free to deal with ordinary social and
economic needs – to shop, wash-up, clean toilets, pay bills and
so on – and those who could not, or chose not to, and who
wished to work on themselves: 'The men who seek the priceless
pearl in the depths of the ocean may drown if no one is topside
to monitor their oxygen supply. They need others to look after
their physical requirements', Schatzman observed.

However, no one at Kingsley Hall saw those who did manage to work with the 'external material world' as 'staff' and those who did not as 'patients': 'No caste system forbids people to move freely from one sub-group to another, as it does in mental hospitals. Nor were people trapped by any institutional power which subordinated everyone to a 'command-obedience structure'. People were free to assume the obligations of a reciprocal bond with another person, or people, or the 'group' and, as free, to dissolve this.

Many years later Laing would recall one man who spent two hours every night slamming doors arguing, when challenged in a general community meeting, that 'time and space' belonged to everyone and that no one had a right to impose silence upon him just because he wished to get a good night's sleep. Another member of the community believed that the PA needed to expand and should buy 300 acres of desert in Ethiopia. This man ran up several hundreds of pounds of phone calls in a few hours, claiming the Ethiopian government would pay for them and when Laing told him he could not use the phone, he ripped the wiring from the wall (Mullan, 1995)

Changing the paradigm

At a conference in 1968, three years after it had begun, Laing offered what he called 'some reflections' on the Kingsley Hall experience. He said that the PA households had 'changed the paradigm', refusing the power of some to define others and of others to be defined in their turn – 'we do not play our part in the game of saying we are not one of them or one of you'. Laing cited two possibilities of experience at the new households – one was the regression gone through by Mary Barnes; the other was what was disparagingly called 'acting out' where people gave expression in actual terms to what they were going though – 'an exploration of possibilities that one seldom allows oneself or is allowed by others'. Laing told of one young man, David, who, terrified for many years of being seen, had decided on a counter phobic strategy in which he took off all his clothes and wandered around naked. He took to painting his face and his body, assuming a series of transformations that were demonic and frightening to others. He was, Laing said, trying to get people to see how he felt and to translate 'into dramatic shared reality the inner "objects" he had always both been terrified lest people know and wanted to know. The impact of this form of communication was a hundred times more than saying "I feel evil" or "I feel I am a whore".' One day another young resident, who went around with a large bird tied to his head, saw this man for the first time and immediately produced a Luger pistol which he aimed at the man's genitals. He pulled the trigger, there was a very loud bang and for a moment no one knew if the gun was loaded or not. David looked down and saw his genitals still there. He was, Laing remarked, cured of 50 per cent of his castration anxiety. Never again was he so terrified. The incident did more for him than the years of analysis he had been having with Laing. 'No interpretations could be as primitive as that dramatic action, completely unpredictable and unrepeatable. At Kingsley Hall we have hoped to have a place where such encounters could occur.' (Laing, 1972)

Schatzman also spoke of the attitudes and actions of the people who lived outside the community – residents were verbally abused as 'looneys', 'drug addicts', 'layabouts' and 'perverts', dog shit was smeared on the floor, windows were regularly broken to the point that the residents decided they would rather be cold than go through yet again the business of replacing them,. The disagreement between those inside Kingsley Hall and those outside was, he said, about morals. Those inside did not conform to society's agreed understanding of 'correct' thoughts, feelings, and so on and ideas about what is good or bad, true or false, dirty or clean. If people did not apply the labels 'correctly' Schatzman asked, did they have the right to live outside a mental hospital. The residents of Kingsley

Hall affirmed their right to do so. Many of those outside disagreed. The residents of Kingsley Hall tried many times to begin a dialogue with those in the neighbourhood. On one occasion several hundred people were invited to a meeting there to talk about the community but only 12 turned up – and by the time they left 'they still did not seem to have grasped the purpose of the "community".' Far more helpful in breaking down distrust was the use of the building by local community groups such as a ballet class and an elderly people's group, These services did create something of a rapport with the local people – 'more than any teach-ins would have' – but the children 'never ceased their hostilities'.[4]

Schatzman concluded his article with the words of one of the residents:

> Those who live here see 'Kingsley Hall' each in his own way … in common to all who live here … is a bafflement or refusal as to fulfilment of 'identity' … the problem is for each to discover some inner need – and to find a way to trust it … It is in honour of this, that Kingsley Hall is: a place, simply, where some may encounter selves long forgotten or distorted …
>
> Does 'Kingsley Hall' succeed? An irrelevant question: it does no harm, it does not 'cure'. It stands silent, peopled by real ghosts, so silent that, given time, given luck, they may hear their own hearts beat and elucidate the rhythm. (Schatzman, 1972: 207)

Local opposition

Hostility to Kingsley Hall came not just from local people but from the local psychiatric bureaucracy and the press. In the summer of 1966 the local Chief Welfare Officer said that it

---

4. In a note to Muriel Lester in November 1964, Laing had expressed the hope that 'a vital reciprocal understanding develop between us and the local people'.

appeared that Kingsley Hall was a home 'for persons suffering from mental disorder' and as such was liable to registration and regulation. The irony was that his intervention followed an article in the *Guardian* newspaper which had been very sympathetic to Kingsley Hall and which had said that about half of the 20 people living there at the time could be diagnosed schizophrenic 'in any other setting'. Laing had to distance himself and the PA from the piece saying the journalist's use of the word 'therapeutic community' had been confusing and that the residents at Kingsley Hall did not consider themselves to be living in such a place. Previously Sid Briskin had written to the local social security office that Kingsley Hall is 'neither a mental after-care home, hostel or nursing home' but simply a 'household' under the auspices of the PA.

Just months before Kingsley Hall closed, the (London) *Evening Standard* weighed in with a major article headlined 'The patients, not the doctors, who decide who gets in' (22 January 1970). Purporting to describe 'a unique mental hospital', the article said it was not the rights of psychiatric patients which were in jeopardy, but the rights of psychiatrists: 'It might be said that the professional directors have committed professional suicide by allowing the patients to decide when they need their help'.

Nevertheless despite its inaccuracies and innuendoes – David Cooper was accused almost in passing of having been involved in groups where violence to others was encouraged as part of a 'liberation of the self' – the journalist, Nicholas Swingler, seemed unable not to be touched by what some people had to say. Did people who stayed there feel 'stronger, better integrated, more able to face the world?' he asked, and answered that some clearly did, including Mary Barnes whose poetic language clearly touched him. Kingsley Hall, Swingler concluded, might never win the argument within psychiatry but people were attracted to it because of its humanity. He concluded: 'A patient [in hospital] may be "voluntary", but no one can disguise that administering an electric shock to a patient is an application of force. It is Kingsley Hall's stress on peaceful self-change in a free environment which makes its brand of psychiatry the one many patients prefer.'

The confusion of the *Evening Standard* article (and other accounts) was understandable, although not its insinuations. There *were* important differences of opinion among the PA members about the value and place of psychiatry. David Cooper, who took up the most extreme position, had titled his book, published in 1967, two years into the time of Kingsley Hall, *Psychiatry and Anti-Psychiatry,* and the term 'anti-psychiatry' was to haunt the PA for the rest of its life, even though Laing (and others) hated the term.[5] Even a reasoned and fair account of Laing's contribution to psychotherapy by a later member of the PA was called *RD Laing and the paths of anti-psychiatry* (Kotowicz, 1997).

The lease on Kingsley Hall came to an end in early 1970, the last residents leaving at the end of May. The Kingsley Hall trustees were shocked at the physical state of their property and claimed a very substantial sum of money, £4,000 (probably about £40,000 today), from Laing himself in order to put things right. The PA questioned the estimate of the repairs needed and pointed out that the Kingsley Hall trustees had delayed their inspection until some time after the last residents had left and that some of the damage was due to vandalism by local people. The Trustees settled after some time for £1,000, still a very large sum of money in those days.

By the time it closed more than 100 people, 119 men and women, had stayed there. The vast majority were in their 20s, nearly all between 20 and 40. Most had stayed for short periods of between one week and three months. Nearly three-quarters had been classified as patients of one kind or another and one-third had been hospitalised. Twelve were hospitalised during or after their stay. Although he would quote such figures, Laing also said they were 'almost as meaningless as the National

---

5. Laing said later he urged Cooper not to use it (Mullan, 1995).

Statistics'. The real point was that 'if someone's not doing any harm to others, is not endangering his or her own life, and does not wish "treatment", "treatment" should not be imposed. At Kingsley Hall no one is "treating" anyone.'

Critics

Since it closed, Kingsley Hall has, of course, not been short of critics, critics from many different perspectives. One of the founders of the PA, Clancy Sigal returned to the US to satirise the whole venture in his novel *Zone of the Interior*. Based around a place called 'Meditation Manor' (transposed from the East End to Brixton in south London) with a Scottish psychiatrist, Dr Willie Last, whose thick accent is rendered in an almost phonetic manner – 'Och, Sidney Bell, is it? Come in mon. It's a pleasure tae meet ye. I've read yir wurk', is how Last greets the novel's narrator on their first meeting. Last, whose favourite authors are Kierkegaard, Jaspers and Sartre, is a man who takes copious amounts of illegal drugs and engages in the most unorthodox activities as a therapist. Sigal's novel was so thinly disguised, and so scathing in its depictions of pretty well everyone who features in it, that it was never published in the UK, only in north America, while Laing was alive for fear of libel action (Sigal, 2005)

From the radical political left, Gilles Deleuze and Felix Guattari, in *Anti-Oedipus: Capitalism and schizophrenia* (1972), criticised Cooper and Laing (and others) for their failure to break completely with what they called 'familialism', and for remaining stuck within an Oedipal framework, whether in their critical analysis of pathogenic families or in 'the constitution of therapeutic quasi-families', an implicit reference to Kingsley Hall (Deleuze & Guattari,1972: 94).

Guattari returned to the attack in 1973 in a review of the French translation of Mary Barnes' book in the prestigious *Le Nouvel Observateur*. Describing the book as 'a confession of disconcerting naïveté', Guattari took Kingsley Hall to task for its failure to go further and for being stuck within the paradigm of the nuclear family. Guattari railed against what he called the 'simplistic reduction of all things to the same old triangle (father, mother and child)'. In this Kingsley Hall had failed to break with 'the bounds of normality within the mould of Oedipal psychoanalysis'. Familialism meant magically denying the social reality. There remain, he said, 'only the possibilities of dreaming and the infernal locked-door of the conjugal-familial system or, still, in great moments of crisis, a little ratty territory into which one can withdraw, alone' (Guattari, 1973).

Guattari's critique of Kingsley Hall, however one may disagree with it, was at least a principled one and based on the experience of someone, Mary Barnes, who had stayed there for some time. Of a completely different order was the attack from the US psychiatrist Thomas Szasz, the highly-influential author of *The Myth of Mental Illness* and *The Manufacture of Madness*. In the pages of the (London) literary journal *The New Review*, under the heading 'Anti-psychiatry: the paradigm of the plundered mind', Szasz took the PA to task for perpetuating in is own way what he called 'the myth of mental illness'. If, as he claimed, there was no such thing as mental illness how could a community exist for 'treating' people, even an anti-therapeutic one? Kingsley Hall, he claimed, was 'Laing's "asylum" for managing madness'.

One of the objects of Szasz's fury was a very brief report by the PA on its work over the first few years of its existence. This report begins: 'This report arises from the communal experience of many people who agreed to be together without pre-defined professional or social roles To all of them, too numerous to mention, this report is dedicated'. Bizarrely, Szasz says this factual and innocuous statement that it is an example of what he calls 'contemporary Western collectivism' where there are no identifiable authors. Not only that 'individuation, self-identification as a form of self-aggrandisement, is denounced at the outset'. It is an astonishing and completely unwarranted inference. Moving on to the PA's founding 'Articles of Association' Szasz claimed they could just as easily be describing the Karl Menninger psychiatric clinic. Instead of hospital beds, Laing's 'factory' (Szasz's word) is called 'residential accommodation'. Szasz then went on to draw the astonishing conclusion from the brief report that people at Kingsley Hall had to pay nothing for being there. In fact of course, everyone who stayed there paid rent, sometimes from savings or income, sometimes from state benefits to which they were fully entitled regardless of where they were staying. In this, Szasz claimed Laing was no different from institutional psychiatrists who imposed a non-reciprocal economic and belittling relationship on 'the madman'. The same economic arrangement characterised Kingsley Hall under different names. Both settings, Szasz claimed, 'reek of the odour of therapeutic sanctimoniousness which the conceit of philanthropy' inevitably exudes.'

> In short, Kingsley Hall differs from the Menninger Clinic (or any other private mental hospital) in much the same way that a flop house differs from a first class hotel. In each case, room and board are provided by one group of persons for another, regardless of what each group calls itself or the other. (Szasz, 1976)

Szasz's article is astonishing in its factual inaccuracy and its determination to make the alleged facts fit his argument. It elicited a long and detailed response from Leon Redler, a US psychiatrist who had come to live at Kingsley Hall, which was published in full. Redler made the basic point that the PA's 'Articles of Association' which so irked Szasz, were written in 'terms appropriate' to the PA's status as a charity under English law. The PA, as the report on its work made clear, wanted to change the ways in which 'mental illness' was seen and described.

Redler also wrote:

non-interesting -

> There were no 'schizophrenic patients' as such at Kingsley
> Hall. There was no one to make and no context in which to
> make a psychiatric diagnosis. There was no binary system of
> patients and staff, surely no formal one. Some of the residents
> had been diagnosed 'schizophrenic' and hospitalised prior to
> coming, others would have certainly been so diagnosed and
> hospitalised had they presented themselves to most
> institutional psychiatrists. Still others had been psychiatrists
> in hospital. No one was in a position entailing obligations,
> responsibilities, privileges and power vis-à-vis others that
> corresponds to the role of staff in hospital. While any
> individual may have regarded himself or any other in any
> number of ways including as staff or patient, that was not
> based on any shared or formal definition.

The members of the PA were, for their part, Redler continued,
responsible to the trustees of Kingsley Hall, but they were not
responsible for the running of the household or the mental
states of the residents. While they differed over matters of
policy in many ways, on the whole they intervened in the affairs
of the household only when there was a serious risk to health
or life or if there was a serious risk to the continuation of the
project, especially from local authorities and psychiatrists.

The *Review* also published a short letter from Steven Gans,
a philosophy lecturer who lived in one of the later PA
communities for a year and a half with his family. Gans, who
would later become a therapist and a member of the PA, wrote:

> We paid our way, as did the other members of the household.
> The house was an extended family which gave people the
> opportunity to re-play and see through their 'numbers'
> (neurotic and psychotic patterns of relating in a critical and
> non-judgmental context). No one treated anyone for anything.
> No one glorified or revelled in annoyance distress or suffering

or flattered or idealised people going through hellish crises in their lives … People opened their hearts to one another and gave each other attention and care … There is, of course, no justification for hospitality except wanting to offer it. Engaging in this ancient and simple act of welcome is, in my opinion, what the Philadelphia Association's households are all about.

Similarly ill-informed was feminist academic Elaine Showalter's book, *The Female Malady: Women, madness and English culture, 1830–1980*. Published in 1987 this claimed to be a work of historical scholarship, a 'feminist history of psychiatry and a cultural history of madness as a female malady'. Whatever its value as such, it was nothing of the kind when it came to Kingsley Hall. Indeed it even seems to have used as source material, not only Sigal's fictionalised account but also Erica Jong's highly popular novel of the 1970s, *Fear of Flying* (Kotowicz, 1997). Showalter's account of Kingsley Hall and Laing's role there is full of inaccuracy and misrepresentation as Showalter tried to fit it into her pre-existing schema where male psychiatrists base their power on their female patients. She claimed that Mary Barnes was 'Laing's only complete case study', which is wrong both in terms of what Laing had actually written and in ascribing to Laing a relationship he simply did not have with Barnes, as Barnes' and Berke's own book makes clear. Showalter's portrayal of Laing was, to one informed critic, 'a concoction of insinuation, rampant prejudice and distortion of fact' (Kotowicz, 1997).

Conclusion

Kingsley Hall has undoubtedly inspired many who have been and are critical of orthodox responses to treating those designated mentally ill. Much of this inspiration has been at the level of ideas as it has proved very difficult to put the ideas into practice, usually for lack of funds. Mary Barnes, for instance, was involved for many years in trying to establish a similar community in Scotland. But at least three important actual projects were inspired by the experience and the experiment that was Kingsley Hall. In the US the psychiatrist Loren Mosher set up the Soteria project near San Francisco in 1971, with an offshoot Emanon starting in 1974. The name Soteria comes from the Greek for 'salvation' or 'deliverance'. Mosher had visited Kingsley Hall several times and took back to the US the idea of trying to break down the distinction between staff and residents who would treat each other as peers and to share the ordinary life of the community. The programme was designed to create a quiet, calming environment that respected and tolerated individual differences and autonomy. Soteria closed in 1983 due to lack of financial support (Emanon had closed in 1980) but has itself inspired several other similar projects in the US and in Europe. (Mosher wrote about his experience of Kingsley Hall and his conversations with Laing in his contribution to Mullan, 1997).

In London, Joe Berke and Morty Schatzman went on from Kingsley Hall to set up the Arbours Association, taking its name from the Biblical name for the places in which the Israelites had found temporary shelter during their exodus from Egypt. After the closure of Kingsley Hall, Schatzman and his wife, Vivien Millet, had opened their own home to people diagnosed (or diagnosable) as schizophrenic and a second community was started in its own premises in Norbury, south-west London. (Berke and others have described the degree of hostility they encountered whenever news got out that they were planning to open a community of some kind, Berke et al. 1995.) The Arbours went on to start a Crisis Centre and longer-stay houses. Although inspired by Berke and Schatzman's experience at Kingsley Hall, the Arbours practice has become much more dependent on mainstream psychoanalytic, especially Kleinian, ways of understanding psychosis and severe distress.

In Scotland the Lothlorien farming community in Galloway, named after the place of healing where time stands still in Tolkien's *The Lord of the Rings*, started in 1974, has acknowledged its debt to the thinking of RD Laing, especially *The Divided Self,* and Mosher (Hickey, 2008).

Any final assessment of Kingsley Hall is impossible. From the point of view of the Philadelphia Association it was the first of its houses and the beginning of its story. Its reputation as part of the 'radical chic' of the era, visited by the rich and famous who wished to be associated with the 'counter-culture' if only in passing, should not be allowed to obscure the fact that it was also a place of serious thought and conversation about the nature of 'mental illness' and the meanings of community. Visitors included not just Sean Connery (at the height of his 'James Bond' fame), but Fritz Perls, the founder of gestalt therapy, Maxwell Jones, the pioneer of social psychiatry and therapeutic communities, and Ross Speck, the innovative family therapist.

Those involved in the PA project had, through their experience, come to the view that what was called 'mental illness' was not something that arose 'inside' people (whatever that might mean) but came about and existed within a very specific social context. It could only be made sense of in that context and its origins questioned within that context. The critique of the idea of mental illness in other words also by necessity involved a critique of the world in which that idea existed.

The political context

Britain in the 1960s was, in many ways, a repressive and oppressive place to live. The criminal law still punished, until 1967, abortion and male homosexual activity. Capital punishment was, until 1965, still in place. The decade had begun with the trial of Penguin Books for obscenity for publishing DH Lawrence's novel, *Lady Chatterley's Lover.* (Prosecuting counsel famously asked the jury whether it was the kind of book 'you would wish your wife or servants to read'.) Until 1968 all theatre plays had to be submitted to the office of the

Lord Chamberlain for his approval and he could demand any changes he thought necessary to protect public morals. Controls on the numbers of Asian and Afro-Caribbeans coming into the country, even though they were British subjects, were already in place and being tightened. And in the British colony of Rhodesia, white supremacists under Ian Smith declared UDI in 1964 to prevent majority black rule. (The same year the Rivonia trial across the border in South Africa saw Nelson Mandela and several of his comrades sent to prison for life.)

Politically the country had been under a Conservative government since 1951. When Labour under Harold Wilson was elected, with a tiny majority in 1964, it was only the second time in the history of the country that a majority Labour government had been in office. The country, like the rest of the world, lived under the ever-present threat of nuclear annihilation. The crisis over the placing of Russian missiles in Cuba and the stand-off between the Soviet Union and the United States had brought this home like never before. All this was being challenged of course – the activist Committee of 100, the Campaign for Nuclear Disarmament, the flowering of cinema, literature and theatre that set out to provoke and to push the boundaries of the permissible. This was the 'bomb culture' described by Jeff Nuttall in his book of the same name which conveys the sense of excitement and fear of one who was very much involved in the radical political/cultural activities of the time, including the discussions around the embryonic PA (Nuttall, 1968).

The PA was also an important part of this challenge to the accepted ideas of the time, although it features little in the many histories of the period which have recently appeared. It does not appear, for instance, in Dominic Sandbrook's well-received and best-selling *Never Had It So Good* and *White Heat*, nor in Peter Doggett's *There's a Riot Going On*. But it moved more directly into the political arena with the Dialectics of Liberation Congress held at London's Roundhouse in 1967. Organised by Cooper, Laing, Redler and Berke, the two-week-long event brought together an astonishing array of radical intellectuals and activists – philosophers like Herbert Marcuse and Lucien Goldmann, anthropologists like Gregory Bateson and Jules Henry, the radical educationalist Paul Goodman, and the black power activist Stokely Carmichael. (Sadly typical for the time there was not one female speaker.) In his introduction to a Penguin Books selection of the presentations, David Cooper said that the members of the organising group, all psychiatrists, had long seen the connection between the processes by which individuals were dehumanised by psychiatry and the wider political context in which whole groups of people were dehumanised. The book was concerned with the analysis of destruction, the self-destruction of the human species and the ways in which men destroyed each other (Cooper (ed.), 1968). The feminist writer Sheila Rowbotham recorded what it felt like to be there:

> In 1967 a strange thing occurred in London called 'the Dialectics of Liberation'. It was a peculiar collection of the incompatible and reluctant forces of liberation. The revolutionary left – or bits of it – encountered the mind-blowers. Having carried both around inside me for some time I was anxious to see how they would meet. It was more of a two-week-long trauma than a conference. I experienced a severe sense of dislocation throughout w... the idea of taking hold of your own definitions struck. So did the tortured delicacy of Laing. (Rowbotham, 1973: 22)

To return to Kingsley Hall, it seems right that, here at least, Laing should have the last word:

> It was not a failure in this respect. That for the time it went on, people lived there who would not have been living anywhere else – except in a mental hospital – who were not on drugs, not getting electric shocks or anything else, who came and went as they pleased. There were no suicides, no

murders, no one died there, no one killed anyone there, no one got pregnant there, and there was no forbidding. Well, that in itself is a demonstration that if other people had been prepared to back that up more, even under those conditions, something was shown there. (Mullan, 1995: 188).

CHAPTER 2

The Community Network, 1970–2006

Some time during the 1970s in a paper called *Asylum*, sub-titled 'A short history of the Philadelphia Association', RD Laing articulated for a general audience what the PA houses were about:

> Suppose you 'freak out', have a 'nervous breakdown', come to the end of your tether, go to pieces, can no longer cope, It can happen to anyone. Where would you go? To whom would you turn?
>
> Suppose you do not want to be jolted out of it, but believe that this is something you want to go through. Who will *allow* you to go through it? Where will you be allowed to plumb the depths of the agony, despair, bewilderment, confusion, perplexity, until a new beginning dawns? No one is asking you to, if you don't want to. But just supposing to feel you *have* to? ...
>
> Suppose one is looking for a *refuge* from all the advice and treatment proposed or imposed by our well-intentioned parents, teachers, doctors, rulers and revolutionaries, who all think they know best what is best for us.
>
> Then one wants an *asylum*, a safe place, a haven, a sanctuary, a shelter. There, one can have, if one wants, a pleasant room of one's own, while other people see to it that there is food, warmth, and shelter, and try to hold the balance between care, concern, attention, mindfulness, and letting be ... .

Anticipating the question what good did it do for very disturbed and disturbing people to live with others who were themselves

disturbed and disturbing, did it not just make them worse, more
disturbed and disturbing and more removed from the world
outside and less able to adapt and function? Laing said:

> I can only say that it doesn't work that way. It seems to work,
> generally speaking, in the opposite direction, if there are a
> few people around who have got themselves together
> sufficiently that they're not going to be thrown into states of
> panic or alarm or anxiety by other people's distress and
> suffering. If they don't feel that they have to do something to
> help other people who are to wanting the help that they feel
> they have to give, and if they are prepared to give the help
> that people want, then we have the provision of an asylum.
> That is to say, a safe place to be when you're a bit scattered
> and don't know who you are or where you are and can't get
> things together for a bit … .

Reflecting on the various PA communities Laing said:

> They have all been melting-pots, crucibles in which many, if
> not all, of our initial assumptions about normal-abnormal,
> conformist-deviant, sane-crazy experience and behaviour have
> been dissolved … With no staff, 'patients', or institutional
> procedures, behaviour is feasible which is intolerable in most
> other places. People get up or stay in bed as they wish, eat
> what they want, stay alone or be with others and generally
> make their own rules. These are places where people can be
> together and let each other be.

Archway community

The weekend that Kingsley Hall closed, Leon Redler and a
number of residents, together with some new people, moved
into a group of short-life properties in the run-down Archway
area of north London. Redler had secured the use of the houses,

which were all scheduled for demolition, from a local housing association. They were located in three different streets but within walking distance of each other and would change as places were taken back for demolition and a new property would take its place. They formed what would be called the Archway community. The community had space for 17 people plus a communal area and also kept open room for someone to come at short notice and stay for a short period of time, say 10–14 days. The community had one meeting each week for residents to talk about anything arising from their living there. The only enforced rule at Archway was that people paid their rent. Otherwise there were, it was intended, no staff-patient distinctions and residents made their own decisions regarding food, sleep, work, cleaning and the degree to which they might be involved with each other. The main aim of the community was 'to enable people to be together and let each other be'.

The community also hosted seminars for the PA network, including residents of other houses and students on the PA training in psychotherapy which had been started by John Heaton in 1970. It was this broader network that the community would call upon when more people were needed to be present for any length of time when someone was going through a particularly frightening or unfamiliar state of mind. The community would also have an 'open house' every two weeks for people interested in living in the houses or in knowing more about their ideas and practice.

Some years later Redler set out his view of the houses:

> People come to our households seeking a safe place to be when their very ability to be is fraught and in question. Sometimes they are in a sudden crisis, usually they have been suffering most of their lives. They have rejected conventional psychiatric treatment as unhelpful, irrelevant or otherwise objectionable. Coming to a place where they might be accepted as they are, and free to find their own rhythm and way of life in community with others, offers them a possibility to stop

holding themselves together in an enervating, futile manner, a chance to let go of ways of isolating and imprisoning themselves. With the development of sufficient trust, habitual ways of relating to self, others and a world begins to change. An opening, a transformation of a way of being may occur. Ways of experiencing and of behaving undergo changes that might be disturbing for people in that position or those around them ...

In our households there are no fixed rules beyond paying rent, refraining from endangering anyone's life or trespassing on the lifespace of others, What constitutes danger and trespassing and how to respond on such occasions is open to discussion and negotiation. We hope that people learn to attend to and care for themselves and each other, come to recognise each other and respond to one another in a salutary manner. In practice, this constitutes the difficult work that residents and therapists must engage in together.

The principle of allowing people to find their own way, in their own time, prevails. People eat, sleep, wake up, get up, stay in bed, come and go, are alone or in company as they chose.

There are regular formal gatherings of residents and therapist to meet, consider the problematics and sometimes celebrate unforeseen joys of living and being together.

'We try', Redler concluded, 'to cultivate a mindful concern that falls between "indifferent neglect" and "ignorant, intrusive interference."'

Asylum

It was in the Archway community that the film *Asylum* was shot over a brief period in 1971 by film-maker Peter Robinson and two colleagues. Robinson had read RD Laing's *The Divided Self* and came to London in 1971 to make two short films about Laing, *Breathing and Running* and *Psychiatry and Violence*. He and his sound engineer, Bill Steele, and cameraman, Dick Adams, moved into the community and stayed for six weeks. Robinson took the unusual step of giving residents the power to veto *before* filming began, promising that no one would be filmed who did not want to be and that people would be shown the material and anything to which they objected would not be used. When they finished filming Robinson and his colleagues returned to the US. Robinson came back to London with about four hours of film which he showed several times at the house but no one objected

The film, running at just over 90 minutes, was premiered in London in September 1973 and was reviewed by the major film critics of the day, a sign both of Laing's standing in the culture at large and of the general interest in issues to do with 'mental health'. It had an impact that is hard to imagine for a similar venture today. At its US premiere a few weeks later, more than 100 people were unable to get into the 500-seat cinema to see it. The showing raised a substantial sum of money for the PA. The film was widely shown at the time, particularly in north America where it was screened at the annual meetings of both the American Psychiatric Association and the American Psychological Association as well as to staff at the National Institute of Mental Health within a few months of its premiere.

Many years later, Adams still recalled the 'remarkably unforced, matter-of-fact spirit of acceptance' of the place and a 'very special ambiance of openness and honesty', while Steele spoke of how being at Archway had allowed him 'to come to grips with my sexuality and open up about it.'

Now available again on DVD, the film is a fascinating piece of history even if it is limited by its form, that of *ciné verité*, then popular among radical documentarists who wanted to show things as they really were, to let people speak, without directorial interference. But what the film gains in descriptive accuracy, it loses in analysis. Ideally it should be watched alongside Ken Loach's film, *Family Life*, made at the same time and influenced by the ideas of the PA. (Loach and producer Tony Garnett spoke to several people involved in the PA houses.[1]) Based on David Mercer's play, *In Two Minds*, and co-written by Mercer, the film follows the story of a young woman, Janice, hauntingly played by Sandy Ratcliff, from her repressed and troubled family to her involvement with psychiatric services, through a Villa 21-type ward to her eventual incarceration in the more orthodox mental hospital where she is given electro-shock treatment and ends up in a catatonic state. It remains a powerful exploration of the issues that the PA, and others, were addressing.

The Archway community lasted in its different variants for several years. By the time it formally closed in 1978/9, just over 100 men and women had stayed there.

The Grove and other houses

In 1972 the PA managed to buy its first property, or at least put down enough money to do so, at The Grove in Stroud Green, north London, a house that remains a cornerstone of the PA network to this day. The deposit was raised at a fund-raising event at the London Hilton organised by Sid Briskin and the actor Suzy Kendall. Those who contributed their talents to the evening included Michael Caine, John Cleese, Georgie Fame, Diana Dors, Marty Feldman, Spike Milligan and Alan Price. The Grove opened in October 1972 when Michael Yocum and his family moved into part of the house. It had room for seven residents. As well as a substantial garden, the Grove also had, at one time, its own pottery for use by people at the house and in the wider network. By the end of 1976, 27 people had stayed there. When Yocum returned to the United States he was replaced by Paul Zeal, although he did not live there.

---

1. See the interview with Loach and Garnett from the radical paper, *Seven Days*, reproduced at www.ejumpcut.org.

Other communities came and went. These included Tollington Park (1973–1978), not far from the Archway community, loaned by a housing association and run by Paul Zeal and Haya Oakley, who had both been involved at Archway, and De Beauvoir Square, run from 1974 to 1978 by Chris Oakley, then a student on the PA training. Joe Friedman opened up a derelict house in Holland Road, west London which ran for several years from the late 1970s. Others were houses loaned by members to the PA, as Leon Redler did with his Crouch End home which was part of the PA network until 1982. That year a housing association property in Bradley Gardens, west London was loaned to the PA and stayed with the Association till 1985. While Kingsley Hall had been in the direct control of the PA which had been formed for this purpose, the houses which followed were financially and administratively independent of the PA, and were run by their own associations of residents.

Hugh Crawford and Portland Road

In 1971 the PA acquired the indefinite use of a property in Portland Road, Notting Hill, west London. This was run by Hugh Crawford, another charismatic Scottish psychiatrist who had known Laing at university and had become involved with the PA on his return from Canada in the late 60s. Unlike Laing who wrote many books, Hugh Crawford wrote nothing for publication but had a great influence on many people in the Philadelphia Association and beyond through his seminars and conversations and his example. Crawford had a very distinctive and profound view of what was involved in the houses, especially the importance of the idea of dwelling, which required time, and a particular kind of attention or attending to. He believed in an approach based on a return to the Christian principle of charity in its original sense of concern which addressed itself to the pain and dread that were part of being in the world rather than to adjusting people to some arbitrary norm. The principles of such a radically different approach were, he said, 'subtle and sophisticated, the practice passionate'. He felt that 'in their small way the PA houses could be a place in which everything human is given a place, a home' (Friedman, 2005: 20) He often quoted the statement by the Roman playwright Terence, 'I am human, therefore nothing human is alien to me'.

'We propose', Crawford said elsewhere, 'merely not to silence the unspeakable'.

Portland Road was a very large house, with space for up to ten people, and by the end of 1976 more than 50 men and women had stayed there for varying periods. The house also acquired an offshoot in the same road. The house had yoga three times a week followed by what was described as a 'loosely articulated meeting varying from the casual to the *intimate*'. There was also a monthly business meeting. Crawford wrote in a report: 'Portland Road proposes to be nothing more nor less than a dwelling, where the boundaries of birth, meeting and play are encountered'. The house came to an end in 1980 after Crawford's premature death and after many battles with the local authority, the Royal Borough of Kensington and Chelsea. (The life of the house is described in more detail in Chapter 3, pp. 42ff.)

Portland Road had been a pivot in the life of the PA, housing, as it did, the PA office and hosting seminars, and its loss was a great blow to the organisation. After this the PA was never again based in one of the houses nor were seminars held there. There was a greater separation between the PA and its houses. The end of Portland Road also coincided with major changes in housing in London. Indeed, some of the opposition to Portland Road arose from the fact that the area had become highly desirable and the existence of a house of this kind was seen as a threat to property values. The era of semi-derelict properties was very rapidly coming to an end. Portland Road was also the last house which would be run by a single person

The loss of Hugh Crawford was an even greater blow to the PA as he had acted in many ways as a counterweight to his colleague RD Laing who had become increasingly detached from the work of the PA while remaining its chair. Laing's personal behaviour had also become increasingly erratic and on one occasion he was accused by some women in one of the houses of trying to rape them. Confronted by colleagues, Laing dismissed the allegations out of hand. He eventually resigned his membership of the PA in 1981.

For a number of years at this time the PA also had the use of a property in the country, Ascott Farm at Stadhampton, Oxfordshire. The house, also run by Hugh Crawford, started in 1977 and had 12 bedrooms and was set in 3.5 acres of land. After Crawford died it was run by Madelyn Brewer, who was on the PA psychotherapy training programme, and the psychotherapist John Heaton, who would visit once a week from London. Ascott closed in 1988 when the PA was unwilling to accept conditions laid down by the local authority. Officials had visited the house and found it unhygienic and had ruled that it was 'an unneighbourly form of development' which had resulted in unreasonable and unacceptable environmental problems and 'distress to young children and their parents' who lived nearby. (One of the occurrences they were referring to was probably the behaviour of one resident who would wet his trousers, then stub his cigarettes out on them so that they smoked. He would then wander down to the local shop in a dramatic cloud of smoke. He said that this was his way of protesting against bourgeois society (Heaton, 2005)).

A PA report on the houses in January 1978 could list four properties that it had the use of, along with a statement about another cottage, in Devon, which seemed likely to be coming into the network's use. (This does not seem to have materialised.) It was probably the height of the community network and there is a real sense of a thriving organisation. There were six people at Portland Road, seven at Leon Redler's house at Mayfield Road, six at The Grove and eight at Tollington Park, although the PA had just been told it had to leave this in a few months time as the housing association which owned it had said the extensive dampness was too costly to repair.

Shirland Road

In 1983 a large house in Shirland Road, Maida Vale in west London was loaned to the PA by Paddington Churches Housing Association (PCHA). The original house therapists were Robin Cooper, who had lived for a time at Portland Road and was completing a PhD thesis on 'dwelling and the therapeutic community', Joe Friedman who had started a house at Holland Road near Portland Road, Chris Oakley and Paul Zeal. The house operated for more than 20 years until March 2006 when it closed after losing its Supporting People funding and no alternative funding could be secured. The house was rocked, as was the whole PA network, by the tragic death of Robin Cooper in a climbing accident in 2002. Some members of the house played music beautifully at his memorial service and one member spoke very movingly of her experience of him as a house therapist in the many years she had lived at the house. After Robin's death the house continued to be run by Joe Friedman and Marie-Laure Davenport until its closure.

Maygrove Road

An unusual project for the PA was the house for a small group of adolescents leaving care which ran from 1983 until 1990. As a result of its reputation of working with difficult and challenging people, the PA had been approached by the Social Services Department in the London Borough of Camden and asked if it would run such a community which would 'promote maturity and independence in a therapeutic ambiance' and to help those who stayed there to move on to more independent living. Maygrove Road was very different to other PA community households in that it did not arise organically from within the PA and the desires of any of its members. No PA member worked in it and the two staff members were recruited and employed in the normal way. That said, many people in the PA gave a lot of time and effort to the planning and management of the project until it closed in 1990.

Freegrove Road

The last PA house to come into existence was Freegrove Road in Islington which was bought in 1995 and opened in 1996 with Mary Lynne Ellis, Heather Townsend and me as the house therapists.[2] Along with The Grove it continues to this day. The story of the house is described in detail in Chapter 4.

The houses were inevitably caught up in the acrimonious row that engulfed the PA from within in 1998/99. As in all such splits the fault lines were many, including different views of what kind of association the PA should be, historical resentments, political ambitions, and personal enmities as well as allegiances. The split was bitter and protracted, and the PA's outmoded structure was unable to deal with the conflict which saw the departure of almost half of the PA membership, as well as many of the trainee group at the time. To many of us who stayed in the PA it felt that there were some, at least, among those who had left who wanted nothing less than the destruction of the PA as a viable psychotherapy organisation and who waged a war through complaint after complaint to the UKCP and who obstructed our validation as a psychotherapy training body. Yet, despite their hostility, some of those who left the PA did not also leave the PA houses. There was a bizarre situation at one point when no less than half of the house therapists in PA houses were not only no longer part of the PA, but had joined a group whose active hostility to the PA went on for many years.

Funding issues

The early communities were run on the proverbial shoestring. They had no external funding and relied on the rent from the people who stayed there and small amounts raised by charitable activities, including a charity shop in London's popular

---

2. A few years earlier a project to get a new house off the ground in Oxford, run in conjunction with a local housing association, had come to nothing at quite a late stage, after a lot of work by all those involved.

what conditions?
a failure in this project?

Portobello Road. Later residents were eligible for housing benefit and, because the provision of housing benefit could be generous, the houses enjoyed periods of relative financial well-being, and were able to weather vacancies and arrears and to pay for necessary repairs and renewals. This came to an end with the introduction of the government's Supporting People programme in 2003. In the words of the Office of the Deputy Prime Minister, Supporting People was intended to offer 'vulnerable people the opportunity to improve their quality of life by providing a stable environment which enables greater independence'. It was intended to provide housing related support to prevent problems that can often lead to hospitalisation, institutional care or homelessness and can help the smooth transition to independent living for those leaving an institutionalised environment.

The PA rather drifted into Supporting People in a mood of wishful thinking, not fully appreciating the possible consequences, despite warnings from some better-informed colleagues. As it turned out, the programme was nothing less than a nightmare for the organisation. It not only resulted in the PA losing one of its longest-running houses but almost lost us another one and introduced considerable uncertainty over the future of residents. It also almost succeeded in bringing the PA itself to its knees. The volume of paperwork introduced by Supporting People made it necessary for us appoint someone as a houses manager where before we had managed through the administrative efforts of the house therapists, backed up by appropriate financial help. PA committee meetings came to be dominated by the endless demands of the programme and the attendant fear that, if we failed to comply adequately, the future, not just of the houses, but of the organisation as a charity, seemed to be at stake. While it may be argued that Supporting People forced the PA to produce policies that it really ought to have had anyway, there seemed to be no end to these and many were either antithetical to our ways of working or just simply irrelevant.

The Supporting People reviews of each house to determine whether they would be granted further contracts with each provider started in 2004. Freegrove Road was the first to be reviewed. Its failure was no great surprise as it had been clear for some time that the house and its way of working had never really fitted into the criteria set by the local Supporting People administering body. Nevertheless we had hoped that a body committed to listening to the people it called 'service users' might be persuaded by the residents (if not by the therapists) that the house was indeed giving them the kind of support they needed if they were to avoid hospitalisation and eventually move on with their lives, as Supporting People stated as its aims. It was not to be. Supporting People was looking for people to be moving on from their 'support' within two years, the idea that people might need this sort of time just to find their way in a house seemed absurd to them, a sort of indulgence even. In addition, the houses did not provide the kind of support it was looking for – practicalities above all else, not reflecting on the experiences that had brought one here, or thinking about one's ways of being with others.

Next to be reviewed was Shirland Road in Westminster. It was a shock when this house failed its review as we had been led to believe by people in the local Supporting People set-up that the house would be fine, that it had managed to reach, at least, the minimum standard required. Again it was not to be and the outcome was a terrible blow to the PA, more so than in the case of Freegrove Road as there we had almost been expecting a negative decision. The loss of Supporting People funding was fatal to the house. We did not own it and the housing association which did and which had leased it to us insisted that we needed to find an alternative source of institutional funding if we were to continue to run it. It would not be possible to try to run it solely on rental income as we were trying to do with Freegrove Road. This we were unable to find and the decision was taken to close the house. While valiant attempts were made to raise money, especially through charitable sources, and to publicise the plight of the house, it was all too little and too late. An excellent item about the house, featuring many of the residents in conversation, on BBC Radio 4's *All in the Mind* programme, presented by the well-known psychiatrist Raj Persaud, resulted in not one offer of help of any kind, financial or otherwise.

The Grove did manage to meet the Supporting People requirements and stayed within the programme until 2009 when the local arrangements changed substantially. That it managed to do so while the other houses did not was a lot to do with the local circumstances – up to a point each Supporting People administering body interpreted the general policy in its own way – and also to the fact that the house had been able to build strong connections with agencies in the locality. It also, latterly, employed a part-time manager solely to help it deal with the Supporting People requirements.

It is not for me to offer an assessment of Supporting People but it does seem odd, to say the least, that a policy whose stated aims were shared by the houses, indeed whose aims were being put into practice by the houses for many years – helping people to avoid (further) hospitalisation and to live more independently – should in practice have had little place for our approach. There is surely also something questionable about a programme that made no allowances for small organisations and which required a mini-bureaucracy if its requirements were to be met.

CHAPTER 3

The Story of a House 1:
Portland Road*

In 1971 a large Victorian house in London's Notting Hill was loaned to Hugh Crawford for an indefinite period for the charitable uses of his choice. The house was held in trusteeship by Crawford for an indefinite period so he had complete security of tenure and no constraints were placed on how it would be used. The property consisted of a basement and four floors and a small enclosed garden. A year after its opening the residents agreed that the Philadelphia Association could use the basement for meetings, training seminars and for its administrative office.

At the start the house lacked even basic amenities. There was no plumbing, the wiring was makeshift and there were only the most rudimentary kitchen facilities. The individual bedrooms were in need of decoration. The garden was reached by walking over an arrangement of planks from the kitchen-dining room. Nevertheless three people moved in and began to make it their home. At the end of the first year, however, only one remained. _turnover_

Even after a lot of work had been done in various ways the house remained spartan and basic. There was never any central heating and many of the rooms, especially those upstairs, were cold in winter. The house never had a TV and music systems only made occasional appearances, never becoming established as part of the life of the house. It was only after a great deal of argument that even a fridge came into the house, and then several years after the house had opened and at a time when a couple with a child had come to live there.

* Adapted from Cooper, 1984

42

Few of the rooms had locks and people rarely used them. Certainly no one fitted a lock while he or she was staying there. There was a basic trust that continues in the other houses to this day, usually much to the astonishment of others. This is not to say that people did not have a great sense of privacy, which some people did, never ever allowing others into their rooms. Even the front door was unlocked much of the time even at night. This was never taken advantage of by burglars or intruders who would, in any case, have found little to take.

Crawford's approach was that the household needed to find its own way. This did not suggest that the house could be left to its own devices, any more than that it suggested that all ways were equally good. The emphasis was on 'letting be' rather than on regulating, ruling or administering.

During the eight years of its existence, some 60 people lived at Portland Road for more than a week. These people became members of what was called the Portland Road Association. This provided a means by which the house could deal with the world at large. It was in this name for instance that the bank account was held and that services such as water and electricity were obtained for the house.

The house never kept records of any kind. No forms were filled in, either on or by those who lived there and people did not come carrying any medical documentation. The only paperwork which was occasionally required was a letter from Crawford in his capacity as a psychiatrist assuring a psychiatric hospital that its patient, if released, would be in a sufficiently supportive environment, or when someone wished to come from another country and their immigration into the UK would be assisted by a letter from a psychiatrist.

Most people who came to the house made their way through some sort of contact with the PA. They had heard of the PA and its work through the writings or lectures of RD Laing. Some also came because they were seeing Crawford for psychotherapy and he felt it was appropriate for them to think about coming to live in the house for a period. Crawford would either suggest the person make contact with the house and leave her or him to take it from there or, in the case of someone more disturbed and highly unlikely to be able to do this for herself, he would do more to facilitate her coming to the house.

About one-third of those who lived at Portland Road had previously been in a psychiatric hospital, most commonly with a diagnosis of schizophrenia or psychosis. Several people came to the house at the start of a psychotic episode, usually from their ordinary living situations, introduced to the house by friends or relatives who were anxious to prevent their hospitalisation. Many people had been in psychotherapy for varying periods before they came to the house and most would, at some point or another during their stay, be in private therapy.

Most of those who lived at the house were single and had never married, although at different times there were two families in the house each with children and each of whom lived in the house for more than one year. About half of the people who stayed did so for more than a year while two people stayed for most of the life of the house. While people came from a variety of backgrounds, rich and poor, educated and less educated, most were white, educated middle class. Some had never worked in their lives, having established themselves only precariously in the world, while others had established successful careers.

Coming to the house

A person who was interested in joining the house would be invited to one or more house meetings in the course of which everyone in the house including Crawford would have an opportunity of meeting him or her. On the basis of these meetings each person in the house would have a say in whether they wished the person to join them. This basic procedure did vary enormously, however. Much would depend, for instance, on something as basic as who first answered the phone when an inquirer called and the nature of the conversations that followed, and of the first meeting which could range from a hurried chat to a conversation extended over a whole evening. It could include an invitation to a meal or involve a visit to the pub over the road. Sometimes, especially when the house was relatively full, a visitor would meet and spend some time initially with two or three people who were able to make themselves available as well as whoever just happened to be around. On the basis of how things worked out with them, perhaps over several meetings, the person might be invited to one of the twice-weekly evening meetings when Crawford visited the house and all those in the house were usually present.

Whatever the actual process, the fact was that a person's joining the house was always predicated upon some kind of interpersonal negotiation between that person and others. People had to find their way into the house, sometimes in the face of considerable apathy or even inhospitality. The person who took an initial phone call, for instance, might forget to tell others that he had invited a visitor to the house, or there would be times when people did not want to meet visitors and would go off to their rooms leaving one individual to play host. Or a visitor would find himself caught up in the crossfire of hostilities between people in the house.

The meetings with visitors were not just about seeing whether people *liked* the person who was interested in joining the house, although this could not be ruled out. It would be an odd thing indeed not to want to like someone if he or she were going to move into one's home. The meetings allowed for matters of like or dislike to be questioned and opened up. A feeling of dislike might reflect some blind prejudice or might be a highly discerning intuition. The meetings also provided a space where a household could decide what it was 'up for', that is the nature and degree of difficulty that a visitor would bring. It was often said that the healthier the house the greater the range of conflict it could accommodate or contain.

The question of how much 'space' the house had at any particular time was not just a matter of how many people were living there, but largely depended upon on what was going on there, who was living there, what they were into and what it opened up. It depended on the mood and spirit of the house at the time. There were times when the house was not full but did not feel like taking on a new member, its primary task at the time being that of getting through its own immediate predicament or overcoming some particular state of fragility. These phases were, however, usually short-lived. There were other phases of tiredness and dreariness when the household might well have welcomed the freshness which a new person might bring but then there would be a dearth of visitors or nothing came of such meetings that did take place. At other times when the house was full and all the rooms taken, the house might be more vital and so keen to admit new people, themselves in great need, that it would even double up the use of bedrooms. Sometimes three people would be sharing one room.

sense of adventure, project, life together

Crawford's place

Crawford did not live in the house and this in itself enabled him to speak from a position of detachment. From his position and from his awareness he was able to see more than others what was going on in the house, the movement or interplay among the residents, and to speak of this directly and provocatively. His position as a psychotherapist was centrally concerned with opening up and encouraging a free discourse. Although detached, Crawford was not disinterested. It was clear to all that while he might leave people to get on with things on their own, his central concern was that the house should thrive. On innumerable occasions he made plain what he thought was good or fitting or best for the house, or his criticisms of how people were conducting themselves in regard to this good. His views carried huge weight, nowhere more clearly than in conversations about new people joining the house. His personal inclination was always to get the house to take something on rather than to play safe, at the same time reminding people that it was their decision and that he did not have to live there. The house would never have taken on so many difficult people without his urging. 'The world is made up of two kinds of people, the freaked out and the chilled out,' he would say, 'and they both need each other very badly'.

It was the practice at Portland Road to have yoga classes twice a week, run by a young yoga teacher who was part of the PA network and who came to be a friend of the house. These were usually held in the early evening on days when Crawford came to the house. Not everyone in the house took part in these classes but those who did were brought together in a situation of a certain sort of intimacy.

The making of bread was something which Crawford also brought into the house. It was illustrative of a particular emphasis he placed on self-reliance and simplicity and on the notion of the 'organic'. Crawford always insisted that a person could, if he or she wished, live very simply or basically in the household. So whatever refinements might be lacking, the house would always manage to see that basic goods such as grains, pulses, vegetables, the basis for simple but nourishing meals, would always be available there. Although it did not always manage to have such staples there was always a large sack of fresh wholemeal flour in a corner of the kitchen. A simple wholewheat recipe found favour within the house and bread making became established as one of the rituals of Portland Road. The making of bread was not, it must be emphasised, introduced into the house as a 'therapeutic activity' or some of occupational therapy to encourage people to get into something with one another or to gain some experience of 'reality' by doing something practical. Nor was it part of an ideology of healthy living or even of self-sufficiency. Nevertheless it came to be symbolic of much for the house about enjoyment and goodness and creativity.

Portland Road was addressed to the opening up of possibilities of living in what Crawford called 'an ambiance of concern'. Crawford firmly believed that a person would find his or her way in such an ambiance if not told what to do, but left free to find his or her own way.

Money

There was, above all, just one (unwritten) rule at Portland Road and that was that each person pay his or her rent. This money was, strictly speaking, a membership fee (of the Portland Road Association) and for this reason, because it was not payment for rental of a room, it was usually referred to as 'dues' rather than rent. The importance of this money was obvious. It was the only source of income for the house which depended on everyone paying their way. Equally important, payment of this money was a clear sign of a person's desire to stay in the house. Each person paid the same amount, £20, each month which covered fuel, repairs and maintenance but not food which was arranged and worked out separately. The money was collected at a monthly 'business' meeting which was always scheduled for one of the times Crawford was at the house. People took it in turns to collect the cheques, complete the most rudimentary book-keeping, and bank the money. Many of the people at the house survived on the most meagre of incomes, usually from benefit payments, or from casual and generally demeaning work. The inability of people to pay or to engage in meaningful conversation about it was something that was tolerated by the house. In eight years only one person bluntly refused to pay the dues. When she had become more than two months behind in her dues and after having refused to talk about the matter, she was asked to leave.

Food

The rituals associated with food assumed a considerable importance for it was around the occasion of the evening meal that people would gather together. It was very much in the spirit of the house that the kitchen and table were communal and mealtimes an occasion for people to enjoy some degree of conviviality. Money or food was worked out in such a way as to accommodate and even encourage a communal table but it also had enough flexibility to allow, up to a point, individuals to do their own thing if they so wished. All food, more or less, was regarded as communal regardless of who had bought it. Each person kept a record of what he or she had spent and at the end of each week the spending was totalled and divided among all who lived there. Those who had spent more received a rebate from those who had spent less. Each person's contribution usually turned out to be relatively small. It was always possible to live inexpensively at Portland Road.

The advantage of this system was its simplicity. Any person in the house was free to help him- or herself to any food in the kitchen. People could eat on their own if they so wished, although take-aways and things bought solely for oneself were not regarded as being within the communal system. In fact, even when some people had more money than others, spending on food was usually kept within the communal plan. There were, of course, endless discussions about what constituted legitimate food expenses, what 'luxury' foods might be included, whether drink was a food and so on. For the most part the arrangement which the house came to, which assumed a certain amount of trust, was never abused.

While the evening gatherings did constitute a sort of focus for the house the meals were not the result of careful planning but came out of a rather casual approach, being got together as often as not by a few people or one person putting together what was available. The house never showed any fondness for a cooking rota, but the price paid for this was that the burden of cooking fell on some people more than others, and a rather thankless task this would turn out to be. Responses to those who did not help, or who helped little, varied according to the perceived situation of those who were less involved, impatience if they seemed capable of doing more but chose not to do so, greater patience if they seemed more depressed or preoccupied with what they were going through, although of course this varied also according to who was actually doing the work.

Similar considerations applied to the question of household chores and tasks such as washing-up or cleaning, attending to minor repairs, keeping the fire going and so on. Here again there was no rota or organisation of tasks. The tasks fell to those who were nudged or persuaded to take them on. People attended to such tasks to very different degrees, according to their different capabilities and inclinations and they did so in very different spirits: lightheartedly, good-naturedly, grudgingly, impatiently and so on. In addition people differed very much in their ability or willingness to invite or ask others to help them. It was not unknown for some people to hog or take over for themselves in a rather greedy fashion some unpleasant chore, whilst complaining bitterly that no one ever helped them.

Boundaries of behaviour

One young man who had spent several years in a psychiatric hospital with a diagnosis of schizophrenia was in the habit of exposing himself to others and quietly and whimsically masturbating, usually to give up after a minute or two with an ironic shrug or a little sigh. When this first happened it was met with an appalled silence. Subsequently when it became clear that he would not be discouraged and since people liked him, his habit came to be met with a certain acceptance. However, when he left the house it caused considerable embarrassment and offence, as it did when he was visited in the house by his parents. People very soon refused to go anywhere with him.

But within the house his behaviour came to be, if not exactly ignored, more or less taken for granted. It became the object of a certain amount of good-natured teasing and dry amusement. It was hoped that he would find his way through to being with others in a way that was less masturbatory. But this proved not to be. He ran away from the house and was brought back several times and finally found his way back to the psychiatric system.

There were three occasions in the life of Portland Road. when a person clearly went beyond the bounds of what the house found acceptable, each involving a matter of serious physical violence. In each case the individual concerned was immediately required to leave the house since it had become clear to others that they were not safe in her or his company. Two of the attacks were made by people who had been living in the house for some time and they were rather unexpected, although the person in each case was extremely disturbed. Neither of these attacks involved a weapon of any kind, no one was badly hurt, and in each case it was with some regret that the person was asked to leave. In the third case, things were quite different in that a bottle was used and the person attacked narrowly missed being permanently disfigured. The attacker was a young woman who had come into the house without having said a word a few weeks previously. Although she had still hardly spoken she had made clear to the house the possibility of her becoming violent and the house had resolved to keep a close eye on her all the time. It was in a moment that this resolve dropped that the attack was carried out and although the complete story of what actually happened was never unravelled, it seemed clear that the victim, who continued to live in the house, had engaged in some degree of provocation. It is significant that the house's decision to accept this woman was the only time that it went ahead despite Crawford's serious misgivings.

Friendship

At Portland Road people got to know and like one another and they did so in ways which went beyond the immediate context of the house, for example going on holiday together or getting to know one another's families. A number of enduring friendships were made and some survived long after the community had gone. Members of the household would enjoy being together; they took pleasure in pursuing common interests and enjoyed a degree of companionship which was unquestionably worthwhile. The company at the house was on occasions convivial, enjoyable, fun. People turned to one another, and asked things of one another, and put themselves out for one another. They enjoyed some degree of give and take which was not simply calculative or exploitative but was grounded upon a genuine liking and respect.

However, friendship at Portland Road was far from a simple matter. It was deeply paradoxical in that the people who came to the house were not yet free in themselves to have friends or, indeed, they were not free because they had no friends. Portland Road was not characterised by the kind of coming and goings of friends and partners that one might expect of a shared house, made up mainly of young and single people. Parties at the house were infrequent and invitations to friends to come to the house, say for a meal, were rare too. Even those who were sociable by nature tended not to introduce friends to the house. Friendships formed within the house tended to have a quality of 'shared insularity' and people tended not to have outside friends who were regular visitors to the house or with whom they chose to spend a great deal of their time. An 'ironic friendship' might arise where two people, backing away from the world, might 'bump into' one another, almost as though no one else would possibly want to be with them.

While people were not free to have friends, they were also not free *not* to have friends. If the opening up of friendship was problematic, then the state of being alone was equally so.

People tended not to enjoy being on their own, not to take pleasure in their own interests, even to find their own solitariness unbearable. Where people found neither their own company nor that of others, to be refreshing or vital, living together became a kind of compromise in which 'having to be friends' with one another or having to assume friendship where it obviously was forced, strained or premature, was a significant factor. This compromise also had something to do with the awful alternative which might seem to be an endless and prolonged enmity with a person one saw and was up against every day.

Sexual relationships in the house were rare. The most obvious reason was that people did not feel they were together enough to get into such a relationship or sure enough of themselves to face the consequences of this coming out into open discussion in the house. The house was singularly ill-suited to the casual affair. The atmosphere of the house, moreover, was one of such highly charged incestuousness that the consequences of any full-blown sexual entanglement which was not sure of its ground might well have seemed altogether too much. While these reasons are true they also miss a crucial point. Portland Road was a house whose overarching discourse was that of analysis. It was not a house *for* relationships but a house *about* relationship. In this sense it was like psychoanalysis and in no way offered a paradigm of human relationship.

Ways of being

One member of the house, a highly sensitive young woman, kept herself to herself, and withheld from the community by living her life in the modality of 'sulking'. This, however, was no ordinary sulk, such as someone might sooner or later be teased out of by simple kindness or good-natured playfulness. It was rather a deeply entrenched and profoundly unyielding attitude to the world which, notwithstanding her obvious capacity for momentary play, entailed a far-reaching denial of desire. Although she was a significant figure in the house and made her presence well known, her position was always one of great fragility, and although most people were fond of her, this was tempered by a certain impatience, since she was always on the brink of leaving. In fact, she did leave the house on a number of occasions but she would find the world able to offer her little solace and would return to remain at the edge of things. As often as not she would eat on her own, and in the summer when most of the house spent a few weeks in a cottage in Wales, she would camp in a field alongside. She did, however, succeed in getting herself off psychiatric drugs and although she did never did quite make herself at home in the house, she was able to make use of it as a secure base from which to engage in psychotherapy. If she herself only tended to enter the conversation on the edges, a great deal of conversation was taken up with the *household's* various responses towards *her*, with the manner in which people made openings for her or else, perhaps with the best of intentions, only succeeded in turning her away.

Another young woman who moved into the house, asked another member to take care of her psychiatric drugs feeling that she could not, herself, handle them responsibly. She subsequently hit a very evident bad patch, asked for the drugs back and took an overdose, from which she was lucky to recover. The person who was supposed to 'help' her had kept his conversations with her entirely to himself, not considering that the matters she was raising were worthy of some discussion with Crawford and the rest of the house. In the course of this whole episode subsequently becoming opened up, it turned out that a precipitating factor in her action had been the thoughtlessness of another supposedly 'helpful' person in the house, who had led her to expect some dependability from him which did not materialise.

Richard was a young man of 23 when he first came to Portland Road. He had been in and out of psychiatric hospital since leaving school and had been diagnosed as having catatonic schizophrenia or a severe and chronic depressive illness. Outside of hospital he had lived for periods on his own and succeeded in holding down short-term and casual jobs. He had also stayed for a time in a therapeutic community run by a large organisation. He displayed many of the features of the classic 'revolving door' syndrome. He had been subjected to intensive and extensive ECT treatments, together with heavy medication, without any lasting signs of improvement. He had now come to feel that these treatments had damaged his brain, his capacity to 'think', and he believed that any further treatment would be 'the last straw'. (There was indeed some reason to believe that the hospital from which he released himself, was preparing to carry out a lobotomy.)

Richard found his way to Portland Road through the help of a social worker who had known him for some years. He arrived one evening by ambulance, looking quite wretched and with very little to say for himself beyond stating that he wanted to 'withdraw' to 'think'. He maintained that he had been trying to do this for many years but he had never been allowed to go through with this. Richard was accepted into the house without much further ado and moved in a few days later. He pottered around the house for a couple of days but gradually retreated to his bedroom in the attic. Richard was to spend the next two years in bed, virtually without moving. He would have been described in hospitalese in the following sort of terms – 'withdrawn', 'negativistic', 'bodily obsessed', 'incontinent of urine and faeces', 'lacking in affect' and so on.

There were occasions during these two years, particularly towards the end, when he would speak to whomever was present with him and from these brief conversations, and from the jottings which he would leave about from time to time, others in the house managed to glean some idea of what he was on about. It all seemed to pivot upon his wish to withdraw. He wanted to be left utterly alone and uninterrupted, so as to be in a position to 'find himself'. Throughout his life, he felt, he had been little more than what others expected of him. Now he was engaged in some last ditch attempt to retrieve, from the silent depths of his solitude, whatever might just be left of his own self. Richard claimed that his life was utterly in balance, on the edge, and that, in order to survive, he had to remain absolutely still. He insisted on being left completely alone. He required absolute silence while he 'thought'. Every sound was to him an agonising distraction. Every move he made was agonisingly critical.

In his writings he again described something of the delicate balance he was trying to maintain.

> I desperately need to put all my energy into facing my anxieties full in the face and battling against any retreat into distractions such as 'displaced anxieties' which prevent me from coping with my real anxieties, make me lose my grip on reality and put me in a state of panic. Noise is a particular threat to me as it's an external distraction I cannot fight, preventing me from thinking and furthering my moments of panic. A loud bang in the night shatters my vision leaving me in a terrifying darkness for about two hours while I work my way back to clear vision.

How could the household help Richard? Presumably by taking him at his word, allowing him to do just what he seemed to want above all – to withdraw. But how was his request to be interpreted? Richard asked for nothing but to be let alone. But he asked this of a company with whom he had chosen to live. It was a paradoxical request. Was the house to acquiesce in it and ignore him? It was difficult to ignore someone who was so close. Were people to tip-toe past his room out of consideration for his rather extraordinary sensitivity to noise? Or was this merely playing into some grandiosity on his part? At what point might others find it appropriate to step in? Were they to wait until he asked? Were they to wait until the smell from his room had become unbearable? Should the house let him starve to death? At one time he was down to five or six stone, wasted and emaciated, stinking, covered with bed sores, crawling with bugs. When was enough, enough?

There were endless conversations in the house on these matters. In this sense Richard for a long time took up a position in the house which was quite central, a fact of which he was doubtless rather well aware. People showed different degrees of interest in having anything actively to do with him, but for the most part there was a general agreement of the sort of approach to take towards him. This was to interfere as little as possible, but at the same time to assume – in the absence of any instruction to the contrary – a freedom to interpret Richard's request to be left alone, as people thought best and not necessarily take it literally. Two people in particular made it their business to keep an eye on him and left food by his bed which he would eat in minute quantities, and they kept him from becoming too filthy. They encouraged some movement of his limbs, and also gave him periodic baths, carrying him, silent, limp and with an expression of long-suffering on his face, to and from the bathroom.

There were many decisions to make. His parents kept visiting and if they had been able to see him there is little doubt that they would have taken him away, there and then, and maybe even tried to have the house closed. Should they see him? What did Richard have to say? Nothing. So the question was put to him, roughly in this way: 'Richard, your parents are here. They want to see you. You won't say one way or another whether you want to see them, so it's not easy to know what you want to do. But you did say when you came here that you wanted not to be disturbed, and so we shall assume, that in the absence of any contrary indication that you don't want to see them now and we'll tell them so.'

In August almost everyone in the house went to the cottage in Wales that the Philadelphia Association had the use of. Richard was clear that he did not want to go; he wanted to be left alone. But the couple of people who were staying in the house did not want to be left with him so he was bundled into the house van with his shitty mattress and stinking blankets. The cottage was smaller than the Portland Road house so there was no chance of Richard getting any peace at all. So now there was a second tent in the field – in the opposite corner of the field – and here Richard spent his days screaming at the sheep because now *they* were interfering with his 'thinking'.

Richard's situation was a very serious one indeed. He was probably quite right in thinking that his life was so delicately balanced. The household too walked a fine line with him. The fact that it finally worked out well is in part due to the fact that the household didn't take it all that seriously. In many ways his stay in the house was a source of much amusement, of which he was well aware. It was without doubt most important to his eventual recovery that, despite his pleas to be left alone, he found himself in a place where life, in some degree of vitality and quirkiness and not just in the sombre earnestness of 'helping', carried on around him.

One of those who looked after Richard, Mike Thompson, who went on to become a psychoanalyst, recalled that after the crisis, Richard explained that he had wanted to be able to count to one million and back without interruption if he was to obtain his freedom. It had taken so long because others kept distracting him by attempts at conversation or playing music or doing something to look after him. When asked why he had not simply told people what he needed, he replied: 'That wouldn't have counted. You had to give me my way, without my having to explain why.' (Thompson in Mullan (ed.), 1997).

Richard's withdrawal and resulting physical deterioration caused a great deal of concern in the wider PA network. Laing and John Heaton, both medical doctors, believed that Crawford was putting not only the man at risk, but the PA too. If he died, they considered, it would be the end also of the PA (Heaton, 2005).

Crawford too was worried as he wrote later:

We worried a lot about dehydration. We worried a lot about bed-sores, which he had developed on a previous occasion in hospital. We worried about him being like that for ever. But we made sure there was always enough water and some food. We bothered. We stayed in touch.

Speaking more generally Crawford commented: 'I do not regard this as a case of someone recovering from a condition which was affecting his mind, but rather as the re-articulation of an individual in an interpersonal context, phased to their readiness for it.'

Crises

In one sense the state of Portland Road was one of continual crisis, either for instance when it seemed too fragile and incohesive to survive, or when it had to withstand attempts in later years to have it closed. But the house also faced crises of a very particular kind, occasioned by the arrival of some person at the start of an acute psychotic breakdown. During the life of the house there were five occasions when its membership included someone who was quite clearly and unequivocally, acutely psychotic and in each of these cases the person had been brought to the house at the beginning of her or his breakdown. In two of these cases the house was not able to hold or contain the person and allow the episode to take its unimpeded course. Consequently each of these people ended up being heavily medicated, in one case in psychiatric hospital, in the other in the hospital wing of a women's prison. In the remaining three cases the person stayed and was held within the house for the full duration of this episode and for the week which immediately followed. This experience enabled those around them to see something of the wholeness of the episode, which was known in the language of the time as a 'freak-out'.

Of the three people, two were already patients of Hugh Crawford, who had been seeing him for some weeks before coming to the house. Both had previously undergone medical treatment for their difficulties. The third person, while British, had been working abroad at the time of his breakdown, and had been flown to London and brought to Portland Road by his family who had had previous contact with the Philadelphia Association.

Each person, at a certain point, seemed to cross some crucial threshold, or undergo some transition, such that they were, or seemed to be, no longer 'getting into' something, or frantically trying to stop getting into something, but were now 'in it'. One behaviour seemed to mark this transition and that was of the person taking off all her or his clothes. From this point the person would remain more or less naked for the duration of the 'freak-out'. This transition, from 'getting into' to being 'in it', although in some ways subtle, was quite discernible. The person no longer seemed to be engaged in a flight, in a frantic state or a running away. He or she now seemed to be completely held by or caught up within some 'movement' which had an autonomy and within which personal volition seem to play a negligible part. There were no longer any furtive dashes to the door or careful little subterfuges to escape from the house when no one was looking. The person did not attempt to manipulate or influence or control others at all, but to take delight in being crazy or wanton. They did not engage in any reciprocity of conversation, nor in any manner of personal relation with one another. They were no longer articulated into interpersonal space. In the three cases this phase lasted approximately two weeks. For most of this time, the person was contained within the kitchen, the centre of the house.

Just as there seemed to be a discernible threshold into the psychosis, so there seemed to be a similar transition out of it. After two weeks or so the person would tend gradually to quieten down, to sleep for longer periods, and to show more interest in food. They would seem somehow to be running out of steam and would hint or suggest that they were beginning or ready to come out of it and to re-articulate back into the world. The particular way in which this re-articulation came about was different for each person.

Each of these people seemed to experience a disintegration, there seemed to be a falling apart of their world. Not only were they unable to maintain or keep up any of their former activities or interests and unable to maintain any effective contact with any other human beings, they were so manifestly and acutely 'untogether' as to be utterly helpless. There was no longer any ordinary world for them simply to be taken for granted, to go on with.

Medical intervention acknowledges that there is no time, no team, no safe place to let things be. This may well be an accurate description of reality but it also implies that there is no sense in letting things be, that this is not desirable. The word 'psychosis' suggest at the person may have retreated to that most paradoxical of sanctuaries – the mind. But it is not some final or even temporary 'inner' resting place to which withdrawal from the world has led. In turning from the world she has not found herself in a haven in which he or she will forever be left in peace. On the contrary, what is most conspicuous about the person who is freaking out is that she is caught up, swept up, or taken away by something, that she is quite helpless in the face of some order of experience which is clearly enormously powerful. It seems to be much less a 'state' of mind or a 'place' that the person freaking-out has got himself into, than a movement whose coursing she is unable to resist.

The metaphor of the 'healing journey' seemed appropriate to the sorts of events as it offered some sort of bearings in a situation which to most people was bewildering, alarming, disturbing and upsetting, provocative and whose outcome was far from certain. It invited people, and perhaps enabled them, to make more sense of a situation which is usually regarded as being senseless. It opened people to the possibility that the person freaking out might, despite her disorientation, become oriented.

In thinking about how the community at Portland Road responded to psychotic episodes it is worth remembering what the house did *not* do. It was not involved in some sort of crisis intervention. Rather the household offered itself as a place of sanctuary, within which the person who was freaking out would be protected from intervention, and would be safely sheltered and held. She would be enabled and allowed, as far as possible, to go through whatever she had to go through. The apparent simplicity of such a statement, however, is enormously deceptive. To ensure sufficient safety and protection for a person freaking out was extremely testing and would have been for any household. For a start it was absolutely necessary that the person freaking out had someone with her all the time. It would have been unthinkable to leave her on her own. This was not about providing company – the acutely psychotic person seems quite indifferent to the presence of others – but to provide protection against injury whether to herself or another. One woman at Portland Road, when there were several people with her, suddenly jumped through the kitchen window to land at the foot of the concrete well some 12 feet below. She was naked and it was remarkable that she emerged with hardly a scratch and seemingly quite unperturbed. The company of at least one other person was also necessary to stop people leaving the house and going out into the street which would inevitably have led to hospitalisation sooner or later. At times this could involve several people where, for example, the individual had to be physically held, restrained, even sat on. It was also necessary to keep damage to the property to a minimum.

At Portland Road a 24-hour rota was organised but, because people quickly became exhausted, the house called in friends from the Philadelphia Association network, including psychotherapists, trainees, residents of other houses and former residents, as well as friends and relatives of the individual concerned.

Without doubt these freak outs were difficult, testing and maddening times for everyone in the house. At the same time, however, they were also exciting times, invigorating, intensely powerful, challenging, and deeply moving. The house was more 'brought together' at times of crisis than at any other time.

Some people came into their own, responding to the crisis in the most unexpected of ways, pleased, perhaps, at finding themselves in a position of being able to be helpful or useful, and pleased to find themselves being taken out of their own miseries. The evening meetings and gatherings played an important part in the 'holding' of the household in these situations, often becoming an 'occasion'. There would sometimes be more than 20 people in the kitchen and the original purpose of the gathering might be forgotten and it would be light-hearted and enjoyable. During such periods Hugh Crawford would stay until the early hours of the morning, most nights of the week. While offering conjectures on what the person freaking out might be into, he stressed that it would be presumptuous for anyone to claim an understanding of the experience. He also stressed the importance of basic things, such as making sure the individual got enough to drink and did not become dehydrated, that people did not get too tired, that enough help was on hand and so on. His emphasis was placed much more on holding than on understanding. At the same time he did draw attention to details that might not otherwise have been noticed, such as things that the person was saying or doing which invited some particular interpretation. It was without doubt because of Hugh Crawford's suggestions, encouragement and interpretations of the situation that the house was prevented from making the most enormous blunders.

While people were understandably anxious to return to their ordinary lives after the freak-outs, Hugh Crawford was always keen that they should stay in the house for a while as he felt this was a time when some important therapeutic work might be done. At this point, for instance, there were often important reverberations throughout the families concerned, and this was not an opportunity to be frittered away or wasted in some flight back into 'reality' or 'health'.

The importance of staying on in the house rather than trying to return to one's old ways became starkly clear after the first freak-out. A young woman from a conventional background, Oxbridge-educated, who was working in the civil service, had a wild and destructive freak-out. She got through it all only to become extremely depressed. It seemed that while some door had closed on her old ways of being, which now seemed utterly empty, the door into any new ways of being had hardly opened at all. She was caught between a past which was now closed, and a future which she could not imagine. She did not know anyone in the house particularly well and appeared lost and forlorn. The role which the house might have played at such a time could have been crucial. Instead, much against Hugh Crawford's judgment, she was persuaded to go for a short break with her family. In the course of a shooting weekend on a country estate she took her life.

The end of the house

Portland Road came to an end with the death of Hugh Crawford in 1980 from a heart attack, contributed to, many considered, by the demands of the household but, particularly, the endless struggles with the various local authorities who tried to interfere and bring the house under their control. As mentioned in Chapter 2, the house was also affected by the rapidly changing nature of the area of London in which it was situated. A visitor to Portland Road now would find it hard to believe that this had ever been anything other than the highly desirable – and very expensive – residential area that it so obviously is now. The existence of a house such as this was seen as a blot and a blockage to the inexorable process of gentrification.

The house closed soon after Crawford's death amidst much confusion. People recalled rescuing significant things belonging to the PA from skips outside, including a set of recordings from the Dialectics of Liberation Congress.

CHAPTER 4

The Story of a House 2:
Freegrove Road

In the late1980s the Philadelphia Association was very successful in raising money with which to buy its first ever permanent home – an administrative office, library, meeting room and consulting rooms – in Hampstead, London. This opened in 1989 and has been the home of the PA since. The same year saw the publication of the first book of papers by members of the PA, *Thresholds Between Philosophy and Psychoanalysis* (Cooper et al., 1989). At the same time, the PA had also managed to raise a substantial sum earmarked for buying a new house, but it was some years before there was sufficient and active interest to make this happen.

A group of people involved in the PA had started meeting sometime in the early 1990s to think about setting up a new PA house. At the time, the PA was run on the basis of weekly meetings, which were open, not just to the small group of full members of the Association, but to the many more associate members, people who had completed the PA training in psychotherapy, and who wanted to be an active part of the organisation. These meetings were not just for the purpose of discussion but had the power to make significant decisions if they wished to do so. In theory the meetings were a form of direct democracy, open to all who wanted to be involved and open too to new ideas and energies. If someone had an idea which they wished to pursue through the PA, the meeting was open to them to put it forward. They had simply to convince the others. As there had been no new PA house since Shirland Road had opened 11 years previously, there was considerable interest in the idea of a new house and support for the energy and desire of the new group. A members' meeting some time in 1994, agreed to make the funds available to the group to buy a property should it find a suitable one.

After looking at several places during 1995 we found a very large terraced house in a residential street, Freegrove Road, in the Holloway area of the north London borough of Islington. The house had been used as a rooming house for single men and was in a pretty decrepit and depressing state, but it was structurally sound and was also relatively inexpensive for the area, which was very central and well served by public transport. With conversion work the house would be a home for up to eight people, a feasible number for a new community. The house would also have substantial communal space, including a new dining area and living rooms, it also had a small garden at the back.

The group involved in getting the house off the ground agreed that there should be three house therapists – Mary Lynne Ellis, Heather Townsend and I, although for financial reasons only two therapists would attend each meeting. The search for suitable people to move into the house started and those seriously interested attended a weekly group at the PA premises in Hampstead. By late 1995 the house had been done up to a high standard of comfort – a very long way indeed from the situation at the beginning of Portland Road described in the last chapter – and opened in January 1996 with five residents, three women and two men. The birth of a new house – and one which was so full from the start – was a considerable achievement and a credit to all those involved, both in the original group and the many more in the wider PA network who had done so much to bring it into being.

The first few months of the house passed without serious difficulty. The residents got on with their lives, people got into, or continued in, their own therapy, most people came to house meetings most of the time which were then held in the new conservatory where we sat around a huge communal table specially built for the house and made of old joists. People who were interested in moving into the house, or at least wanted to give it serious consideration, would come to one of the weekly meetings, sometimes for many weeks before making a decision or just drifting away. A sixth person moved into the house not long after it opened and a seventh moved in during the autumn. The eighth place was never filled. As in other PA houses, there were no rules other than to pay one's rent and refrain from violence to others. We did strongly urge the residents to set up a food kitty as a minimal level of communality and in the hope that this would lead to some shared meals at least.

There were, of course, problems and it was not unusual for one or other of the therapists to be called at home by one of the residents, feeling he or she was unable to cope. Very occasionally one of us would actually have to go over to the house to talk with someone or to try and sort something out at least for a time. Very early on we also had to deal with a strong move by most of the residents to get one resident evicted, a classic case of scapegoating in which the residents firmly believed that the women's expulsion would restore the house to the unproblematic state it had enjoyed in its halcyon first few weeks. This too we were able to think and talk about and the woman stayed. Slowly the life of the house began to establish itself. It was not long, however, before the house was hit by its first serious crisis.

Manic episode

In early summer 1996, one of the first residents, Jane, went into a very serious manic state. She had not told us that this might happen, only that she could and did become 'depressed', but it later became clear that it had happened before. Jane had not been at a couple of meetings but in itself this was not particularly unusual and in itself gave no cause for concern. On a Thursday I was called by people at the house who were getting increasingly concerned, not so much about what she was doing in the house, which they were prepared to try and contain, and help her get through without doing too much damage to the house and not hurting herself. They were more concerned that Jane would leave the house naked or cause damage and distress to the neighbours. When it became clear that things had gone too far I was called.

When I got to the house and saw the state Jane was in, running around with no clothes on, completely unreachable, setting off the fire alarm and breaking things, I was amazed that the other residents had been able to deal with her as they had. But it quickly became clear to me there was simply no alternative to her going into hospital, although people in the house were all very reluctant to accept this, even at this stage. Gone were the days when the PA network might be able to come in and help the situation. As it was I could not even contact colleagues for advice as everyone was at the weekly PA meeting. (This was before people had mobile phones.)

In the end the police were called by neighbours some time around midnight and, worried that Jane might have glass or something else she might use as a weapon either on herself or against them, entered her room with riot shields to take her away to a psychiatric hospital after the duty psychiatrist had agreed to put her on a section.

The incident was deeply upsetting for everyone in the house at the time, to have witnessed Jane in such an alarming state and then to have witnessed her being bundled out of the house by several large police officers, covered only by a curtain that she had torn down in her room, and taken away in a police van as the ambulance which had arrived was deemed not secure enough for her. Jane, however, did come back to the house after several days in hospital and stayed there for some time. She would later complain to the PA about the house therapists' actions, not that we had had her hospitalised, but that we had failed to do so earlier. There was no recognition on her part that she had in effect deceived us by not telling us the truth of her condition and of what was likely to happen if she failed to take her medication. (Many years later I happened to see Jane on a TV news item saying that people should not be compelled by law to take psychiatric medication, that they had a right not to do so. This was – and is – a perfectly acceptable position of course but one that has to consider what is to happen when this results in considerable damage to a place that is the home of other people.)

There was, in the event, no criticism from our colleagues about what had happened and how we had dealt with it. Those who had had anything to do with the houses over the years knew only too well how this kind of situation arose and how little there was to do be done about it. People in the houses often had no resort but to go to hospital for a time. It did seem a pity, to put it mildly, that this sort of experience could not have been shared before the crisis, but could only emerge piecemeal afterwards That it was not highlighted the strange absence of any tradition within the PA in which the experiences of those who had worked in the houses was shared with people who had come to the organisation more recently, whether on the training itself or in any other forum.

Therapist difficulties

Difficulties of a different kind began to emerge within the therapists' group itself. To its considerable credit the PA had entrusted a new house to a group of people with hardly any experience of the houses. Apart from one who had done a short time as a maternity cover replacement, none of us had any experience of working in a PA house. As we have seen, PA houses have often spoken of providing a space where people might just be, of letting them find their own way without being told what to do. My colleagues, however, seemed to be much more self-consciously 'therapeutic', seeing the task of the therapists to make interpretations, to explain what was really going on to people who did not understand or who lacked insight. The residents seemed to be seen as *only* vulnerable, distressed, and in need of protection. At times, it seemed to me, they were in danger of being infantilised. As is so often the case a little incident is telling. A few months after the house opened, I had to travel to Glasgow for the funeral of an old friend who had died suddenly. I was unable to come to a meeting and asked one of my colleagues to explain my absence to the house. When I returned I discovered that they had judged this inappropriate information and had told the house that I had some family matters (or some such) to deal with.

It seemed impossible for me to work in the way I had hoped. I wanted to find my own way, just as we were supposed to encourage residents to find theirs. (The 'dynamics' of the therapist group were further skewed by the very close friendship between my two colleagues.) After eight months I decided finally to stop working in the house, saying I would stop in August 1996 when I was due to take my summer holiday. We told the house only that I was doing so for personal reasons.

My departure as a house therapist so soon after the house had opened caused several colleagues to ask questions about what was going on in the house. They were met by a refusal by the house therapists (and by their supervisor) to speak about this on the grounds of 'clinical confidentiality', or that the remaining therapists were being victimised. It should be made clear that no one in the PA was asking inappropriate questions and no one was asking about any individuals living in the house, so the response of clinical confidentiality seemed out of place, spurious even. This house, they said, was a PA house, bought by the PA, and the therapists were paid out of rents that came to the PA and were being supervised by someone who was a senior member of the PA. The PA members had a right to know what was going on in their name. But it seemed impossible to have an open and honest conversation.

'New PA/old PA'

Even before the first residents had moved in, the new house had begun to be the focus of concern among some in the PA. Concerns were being expressed that the new house was in some way not just ideological, explicitly aimed at redressing social and political inequalities, but oppositional to the PA's traditional approach. Indeed, some of those involved in the new house, in an echo of political developments in the Labour Party at the time, would refer privately to the new project as being 'New PA' as distinct from 'Old PA'. 'Old PA' was seen – and portrayed – as being anarchic, living in the past, isolated, slightly paranoid even, unable to work in the modern world dealing with agencies in the mental health system. There was, it should be admitted, just a little truth in this characterisation of the existing PA, but in the end it was a caricature. Ironically – and predictably – the 'New PA' would develop its own version of the paranoia seen in others, as the new project had to be defended against those who did not understand it and who, through their questioning, were seen as being interfering, oppositional and obstructive. At the same time some of those who felt they had put in the most work seemed to become very protective of the house and to regard it as 'theirs' and it became increasingly difficult and eventually impossible for others to question aspects of the house. In truth of course it was, as people kept saying, a PA house, which the PA had paid for, and a project to which many people in the Association had contributed a great deal of time and effort

The notion of 'New PA' was never explicitly articulated. If it had been it is hard to see how the PA would have agreed to the creation of such a house. But it was not just a matter of rhetoric but affected the very conception of the house For instance, at one meeting before the house opened, Joe Friedman, an experienced house therapist at Shirland Road, had questioned the idea of the house having an entry-phone system. This was not, he pointed out, normal practice in an ordinary home, which would usually just have a door bell, but the sort of thing that would be found in an institutional 'home'. The question, however, was taken as showing a lack of sensitivity, especially towards female residents. (In the event, the entry-phone system was installed, only to stop working pretty soon afterwards and to fall into disuse.) So too when, over a weekend in January 1996, many people from the PA network turned up to do the last jobs at the house – hanging curtains, assembling chairs and beds, putting up lights and so on – the people who were actually going to live there had not been invited to come. Things were being done *for* them, not with them. Similarly when an event was held at the house for local mental health and other agencies just before any residents moved in, this took place without any involvement of the residents themselves. They, symbolically, turned up for the first meeting to take place at the house an hour or so after the networking event had finished.

The questions that were being raised about Freegrove Road, especially about the accountability of a PA house to the organisation which owned or it, became part of the serious difficulties that were emerging within the PA and which would lead eventually to the split in 1997/8, mentioned in Chapter 2, which resulted in the loss of more than half the PA's members and the formation of a new organisation, the Site for Contemporary Psychoanalysis. The name of the new organisation confirmed to some what a part of the difficulty had been, that our erstwhile colleagues saw their primary theoretical loyalty to a particular system of thinking, psychoanalysis, whose place in the practice of the houses was far from unproblematic.

Crises

As the house neared the end of its first year, another of the original residents, Jennifer, was admitted to the local hospital after taking an overdose at the house. Jennifer was one of those people who had come to the PA having read Mary Barnes' account of her time at Kingsley Hall and, in the early days of the house, would occasionally seek refuge in the large and unoccupied cellar. She returned to the house for a meeting and spent some time in her room before going back to the private hospital to which she had been transferred and where she was supposedly under a close watch. A few days later the house was informed of her death by hanging. Two letters were found in her room, one settling her rent up to the time of her planned death, the other asking that her ashes be buried in the garden at the house. How bad relations had become between me and my erstwhile colleagues was clear when my former colleagues refused to pass on to Jennifer's parents a letter of condolence I had written. The letter was returned to me with a note saying they did not know what was in the letter and would not wish to be implicated in it.

Townsend and Ellis carried on working at the house till spring 1998. When they stood down they were replaced by a new group of therapists. This group too would encounter difficulties among them that would prove intractable and eventually resigned.

One of the most bizarre things the house had to deal with during this time was a legal action against it by one of the existing residents. Peter, one of the original residents, had not been coming to meetings, nor responding to messages about the importance of this. In early September 1998 he issued a summons against the PA and the housing association which then managed the house on behalf of the PA, claiming that they had failed in their duty of care, failed to deal with crises in the house, 'allowing tenants to endure harassment and distress in crisis'. Peter had previously made a fairly generalised complaint to the PA about matters at the house and this had been considered very carefully. Attempts to resolve this by getting him to come to meetings or to meet separately with the therapists or a member of the PA, or indeed anyone he wanted, came to nothing. Peter's claim, not surprisingly, was thrown out when it eventually came to court, but the whole business cost a huge amount of time in dealing with solicitors and money, over £3,000 in the PA's legal fees. Peter himself had no money, was legally aided and could have continued his legal campaign for a long time. In the event he agreed not to pursue the complaint, but only if the PA agreed not to pursue him for costs. The sorry business showed clearly to those involved in the houses the continuing reverberations of Jennifer's death and Jane's manic crisis and eventual hospitalisation in the first year of the house, both of which Peter had lived through. Jane herself had supported Peter's case, claiming in an affidavit that the PA therapists had failed to deal with her situation, in effect that she had not been hospitalised much sooner. It is likely too that Peter was affected in some way by the early difficulties among the therapists, although we did a great deal to keep this from the residents.

Over time a situation developed at the house which was antithetical to the spirit of the house and threatening its very existence. House meetings were sparsely attended and internal dynamics among the residents were making it impossible to get more people into the house. Many visitors were met, not with welcome, but with considerable hostility and did not move in. Some of those in the house had serious problems with alcohol. This coincided with the house therapists wanting to stop working there. The PA considered the situation so serious and intractable that it made a decision to close the house and take some time to think about its future. Fortunately for the Association the remaining few residents were found other accommodation relatively quickly. A decision was made to reopen if new house therapists could be recruited and if enough new residents could be found to make the house viable. Christina Moutsou and I were appointed house therapists in late 2002.

A second start

The house reopened in March 2003 but we did so with only
two female residents. We had planned for a minimum of three
people, but a third woman pulled out at the last minute. (She
was to move in much later.) It was a very shaky (re)start indeed
and in normal circumstances we would have deferred the
opening of the house, but there was pressure from within the
PA either to open the house then or not open it at all. Within a
couple of months the original two residents were joined by
two others, a man and another woman. The new house slowly
began to establish its own ways of being. Residents ate together
sometimes. People carried on with their voluntary work outside
the house. Someone brought her pets. (House meetings were
sometimes attended by a rather large rabbit.) People who were
new to London spent time getting to know the area and the
wider city. Over the house's first summer someone who had
come from the country took others back there. At some point
the residents decided to break with the past and end the house
meetings around the communal table in the conservatory to
the comfort of the living room. There were rows and arguments
and fallings out, but also friendship and concern, for one
another and for the house. There were communal meals and
people marked each others' birthdays. Most people came to
most house meetings. There was, most of the time, a sense
that enough people wanted the house to thrive and were
prepared to do a lot to make that happen.

Sadly, just before its first Xmas, the new house was shaken
by the suicide of the one male resident, David, who was in his
40s, had a history of terrible persecution and had been referred
to the house by his psychotherapist in the West Country where
he had been living for many years. Although he could be quite
involved in the house at times and had been close to one of the
other residents, David became more and more withdrawn. He
stopped coming to house meetings and, we learned later, had
also stopped his own therapy. When he spoke, which he did

little, it was to talk about the possibility that he would return to the West Country, so no one was unduly concerned. We hoped that, in time, he would find his way back to the house meetings and an involvement with the house. Just before Christmas, however, he had gone to a block of flats near Ladbroke Grove, west London, where he jumped off, killing himself instantly. We found out later that his father had once lived there.

David's suicide was a great tragedy – but it was not a terrible surprise as some of those who knew him before he came to the house said it was. It seemed, his only escape. ('The dreams in which I'm dying are the best I've ever had', was a line from the 'Mad World' song at the time that kept going round and round in my head.) But it was a terrible blow to all of us involved in the house, residents and therapists, and all of us felt great sadness. All of us involved in the houses inevitably questioned what we were doing, what good did it do. Personally I felt guilty too as it had been I who had met David for the first time following his referral to the house and I had strongly encouraged him to come, believing that he would benefit from being there. Indeed, two nights before he died, David had appeared at my home (where we had first met) out of the blue. He said very little but did say something about wanting to go back to the West Country. We had a brief conversation and eventually I said I would give him a lift back to the house, a 20-minute drive away but much more difficult by public transport. By the time I had put on some outdoor shoes and found the car key, David had disappeared from the house and the street. He was nowhere to be seen. To my considerable relief he did turn up at the house later that evening. The next evening, while I was at a very fraught meeting at the PA, David showed up again at my home. Finding I was not there, he walked off and went into a nearby police station. He was asked to wait but went off again before anything could be done and then must have walked down towards Ladbroke Grove, a 15-minute walk, where he threw himself off the building.

David had no family that we knew of and only a few friends in the West Country, so it fell to the house to organise the funeral and to deal with the coroner's office. The funeral was a bleak affair although everyone was touched, I think, by how loved David had been by the few people he had known. The residents organised food and drink at the house for after the funeral and the event was a chance for everyone to share their very different memories of the man they had known. The inquest, shortly afterwards, concluded that his death had been suicide and, to our considerable relief, made no criticism of the PA for failing to do anything.

David's death also shocked the wider PA network and those of us involved in the house were greatly touched by the concern and sympathy shown by colleagues. One colleague who had been involved in the houses for many years said that, while it was indeed a terrible thing, it was remarkable that it happened so rarely, given the kind of people who came to the houses and the kinds of histories they were trying to deal with. My colleague, Christina Moutsou and I were relieved that we heard not one word of criticism from anyone in the PA. Indeed there is nothing I would have done differently. I would still have encouraged David to come to the house, still advised him to be in therapy, still hoped he would come in time to trust us all a bit more than he was able.

During this period it proved very difficult indeed to find suitable people to move into the house and numbers remained low for much of the time. It seems clear that word had got around possible referral sources that the house was struggling and many believed that it would not survive and that it was simply a matter of time before it closed. There was little point in suggesting anyone went there. Several people did move in but they did not really get involved in the life of the house and then moved out again. At least three of the men who moved in had serious alcohol problems which they had managed to keep from us and which would come to cause real difficulties for the house before they eventually left. Two in particular could also become very intimidating. One of these men had kept from us also a history of violence which, had the house known of it, would have been highly unlikely to offer him a place. It is always easy to be wise after the event and it is easy to think how naive we all could be. At the same time we wanted to give people a chance and this man came into the house as a result of our openness and trust.

Another person to whom we wanted to give a chance was Rachel. Young for us, volatile but with an apparent desire to be different, she very nearly killed herself through an overdose. She did not die only because one of other residents, fearing she had done something after a row on the phone with her parents, went into her room and found her. She and the other residents got her to hospital and stayed with her and went to see her in the days afterwards before she came back to the house. That she failed to kill herself could have been a turning point for Rachel, but she was unwilling or unable to look at what had led to her overdose and ended up resenting the care and affection she had been shown by people in the house and stopped coming to meetings. In the end we had to initiate legal proceedings to get her out and we (and she) were fortunate that other, more suitable accommodation was found for her.

Soon afterwards Jeff, someone we had accepted into the house some months previously with no knowledge of his history of violence, started drinking heavily and also taking drugs, something he had stayed away from for over a year. He too stopped coming to meetings, stopped going to therapy, and became increasingly threatening in his manner. He 'borrowed' a substantial sum of money from the house which he never repaid. Fortunately he would spend little time at the house, staying with friends, but one Easter weekend when my colleague Christina was out of the country and I was going away for the night to the Cotswolds with my family, he decided to spend some time there. I started to get a stream of anxious calls from people at the house, worried at his very noisy presence and his threatening behaviour to several people there, the men in particular. It seemed highly likely that I was going to have to drive back to London in the night to try and deal with him, although quite what I was going to do was another question. I did try to calm him down over the phone, assuring him, among other things, that a pair of jeans he had bought and claimed had been taken by another resident, would be replaced by the PA. (Needless to say they eventually turned up in his own belongings.) I advised people to consider going to stay at the PA house at The Grove and also to contact the local police and let them know what was going on and not to hesitate to ring 999 if they felt in any way seriously at risk. In the event Jeff's presence that night passed without incident and he left soon after.

Jeff's brief stay was a salutary lesson to us all. We had all had our doubts about him. He had had a very troubled life and seemed serious in his attempts to deal with it. He had come to us after completing a very challenging year at the Henderson Hospital and was keen, or so it appeared, to carry on the intense therapeutic work he had started there. Yet there had been something hidden about him during the application process and what this was became evident once the honeymoon period of being in the house had come to an end.

External threats

As we saw Freegrove Road was bought by the PA on the basis that it had room for eight people. Very early on in the life of the house we were told by the local authority, Islington Council, that we were allowed to have only six residents, not the eight residents the house had been bought for. Any more turned the house into what the council regarded as a 'multi-occupancy dwelling' for which planning permission was required. When applied for, however, this was refused on grounds that seemed to us quite unclear. At this point the need to have at least the possibility of having more than six residents was not primarily financial, but crucial for the sense of community. Later on however the local authority restrictions would have even more serious consequences for the house's viability. It was only in 2006 that the house was able to secure permission to have seven residents. It should be said that nothing had changed in the house. Physically it was exactly as it was when it had opened in 1996 and had no new amenities. This time round, while the council officers were supportive of our application and would have passed it on their own authority as they were permitted to do, a number of local residents objected, as was their legal right. Their objections delayed the decision which then had to go to a meeting of the planning committee. It was striking however that people who had been happy to object by email were not prepared to show up in person at the committee meeting to argue their case – as did representatives from the PA and the house – and the decision went in favour of the house. We were delighted by the decision but the fact that people in the street objected to the house being there was highly unpleasant. It should be said that there had been very few problems with neighbours over the years. One year the house decided to have a new year's eve party and, as it was not cold, people were out in the front yard. Someone who lived in the road came by, stopped for a drink and at one point in the conversation said to one of the residents, 'This used to be a house for mad people, you know.'

A few months after the house reopened in 2003 it faced another major setback in its attempts to establish itself. This came when the funding, under the new Supporting People arrangements, was withdrawn. The decision, described in Chapter 2, was not, as we said, a surprise but was nevertheless a real disappointment and a setback in our attempts to establish the house.

With the Supporting People money withdrawn, with very little notice it should be said, the house was forced to go to the PA and ask for financial support from its central funds to help it until such time as it was able to become self-sufficient. While this was agreed by both the PA's Council of Management and by its trustees the payment caused a great deal of resentment with some members, even though the PA had substantial reserves and was in no way financially compromised by making the payment. Once again, some colleagues claimed, the PA was just subsidising the house therapists who had used their influence to get what they wanted. Others, albeit a very few, claimed that the time of the houses as such was over and that Freegrove Road should be closed and either sold or rented out commercially, although it was never spelled out what might be done with the money and how this would be meeting the PA's charitable aims. The house therapists also argued, correctly as it turned out, that if Freegrove Road were sold or closed the PA might easily end up with only one house, as we could not be sure of how Shirland Road would fare in *its* forthcoming Supporting People review. If it were to fail the PA would be left with only The Grove.

It was around this time that the house also lost a substantial grant from the local health authority. The money, several thousand pounds each year, had been used, among other things, to help residents pay for their own personal therapy. Looking for savings, the health authority simply informed us a couple of months in advance that it was coming to an end and that was that. The money, a small amount to the authority but significant to the house, would have helped significantly to meet the house's deficit.

No one was trying to close the house but the actions of several did nothing to make it any easier and, in some cases, did threaten its existence.

This short account inevitably tells only a small part of the story of one PA house. It is, ironically, much easier to narrate crises and difficulties than it is to depict ordinary life. And yet around the tragedies and serious difficulties narrated here, this more ordinary, everyday life of the house went on for most of the people who lived there, many of them for substantial periods. They shopped, ate, cleaned, went to the pub or the

81

cinema, stayed in their rooms, had parties, argued with others, made up with others, made friends, made enemies, started courses, gave up courses, went away, came back, looked after the house and each other. It was the many residents, after all, unnamed here, who cared for Jane and Jennifer and David and Rachel and all the others as they were actually living with them. That the house survived is a testament to *their* kindness, *their* concern and *their* resilience.

CHAPTER 5

Hospitality, Dwelling and Home

The Philadelphia Association came into being in order to put into practice what was a relatively simple idea, that of providing places of asylum as an alternative to the psychiatric hospitals and other treatments of the time. Kingsley Hall and the communities that preceded it and those that followed did not arise from, or follow, a theoretical position or stance, but arose as a practical response to a need. The practice went hand in hand with the articulation of a critique of the existing dominant practice – the so-called medical model of psychiatry – and of the elements of the alternative, of what was involved in the provision of asylum. This articulation has continued to this day and in this chapter I want to look very briefly at some of the ideas that some of the people involved in the houses have found useful in thinking about what we do.

Home

We are all too familiar with the travesties of official places called 'home' whether these are children's homes where children have been abused, or care homes where the elderly or infirm are ill-treated or neglected. Our houses have never been homes in this way and we have never chosen to become registered as such. We have preferred the financial uncertainty and insecurity of being outside the 'care home' system, potentially quite lucrative, to being told what we can and cannot do, and how we should do it.

Despite its devaluation, the idea of home is central to what we do. We cannot make people feel at home but we do our best to provide the conditions to make it possible. We do this through hospitality, by offering a welcome. Hospital, we might recall, originally meant guesthouse or shelter for the needy, and only later came to mean an institution of the kind we think of now. Hospitality meant friendliness towards guests. Of course, hospitality carries risk. One never quite knows whom one is inviting in to one's home, how he or she will respond to the hand that is extended. We see this over and over again in the PA houses. On occasion the risk is one of personal violence. John Heaton recalls how at Ascott Farm, he was threatened by two men holding bicycle chains because he refused to agree with their demand that they be allowed to sleep with the women in the house because of the deprivation they had suffered in their lives. The women themselves did not see why they should be required to make up for this lack. The men desisted only when the police came. More recently, I was told by one resident how close I was to being 'glassed' for something I had said in the course of a meeting and on another occasion the same resident was very serious indeed in wanting to take me outside 'to sort things out'. At times houses have even taken to having plastic cups at meetings fearing the throwing of glasses or china mugs.

A more common risk than that of personal violence is violence to the physical fabric of the house. We saw how shocked the trustees of Kingsley Hall were at the state of the building when it was handed back to them at the end of the lease. Probably all the houses have experienced some violence of this kind.

The risk may also be to the continued existence of the house. It is striking how often residents, from Kingsley Hall to today, have simply failed to pay their rent and left owing substantial sums of money to a community that can ill afford it. It is striking too how often the PA has had to resort to legal action to remove residents who have refused to leave, even after a house had come to an end.

The philosopher Agnes Heller asks the question, 'Where are we at home?' and responds:

Home sweet home – but is it so sweet, or has it been so sweet? The familiar fragrance can be the smell of burning flesh. The familiar gesture can be the hand raised to beat. The colour can be dark and grey. Home is where we were weeping, but no one listened, where we were hungry and cold. Home as the small circle one could not break through, the childhood that seemed endless, the tunnel without exit. It was, after all, in a world where we all had a home where the metaphor of the earth as a valley of tears so full described our experience. How good not to return, not even on the couch of the analyst. (Heller, 1995: 14–15)

We cannot make people feel at home but we hope that they may come to feel more at home in themselves and in the world. The two are subtly and complexly linked. One does not follow the other, but they take place together. Familiarity, Agnes Heller writes, is a matter of being accustomed:

Familiarity provides the basis for our everyday activities, and at the same time it is an everyday need. Integral to the average everyday life is awareness of a fixed point in space, a firm position from which we 'proceed' … and to which we return in due ours. This firm position is what we call 'home' (Heller, 1984: 239)

Home, of course, is not just a matter of a roof over one's head and a family. People, Heller reminds us, may well have these things but not feel at home. Familiarity is not the same as being at home but is one of its ingredients.

Over and above this, we need the feeling of confidence; 'home' protects us. We also need the intensity and density of human relations, the warmth of the house. 'Going home' should mean returning to that firm position which we know, to which we are accustomed, where we feel safe, and where our emotional relationships are at their most intense. (ibid)

This familiarity is not something that is given, but something that has to be achieved. As the philosopher Emmanuel Levinas puts it, unlike other possessable goods, the home is possessed precisely because it is hospitable. Hospitality is an accomplishment. (Levinas's major work, *Totality and Infinity* can be read, Jacques Derrida has suggested, as 'an immense treatise on hospitality'.)

Home, Levinas reminds us, is not an 'indifferent somewhere' but rather a base or condition; to exist *is* to dwell. The privileged role of the home does not consist in being the end of human activity, but in being its condition, its commencement:

> Man abides in the world as having come to it from a private domain, from being at home with himself, to which at each moment he can retire … Simultaneously without and within, he goes forth outside from an inwardness, the subject contemplating a world presupposes the event of dwelling, the withdrawal from the elements (that is from immediate enjoyment, already uneasy about the morrow) recollection in the intimacy of home. (Levinas, 1969: 52–3)

For Levinas this familiarity or dwelling is in itself existence: 'To exist means to dwell, in the sense of a recollection, a coming to oneself, a retreat home with oneself as in a land of refuge' (Levinas, 1969: 156). Such familiarity is not a given but an achievement. The recollection that Levinas speaks of is a 'having time'; it is 'precisely to have time'. Recollection indicates a suspension of our immediate reactions to the world. Thus the habitation or dwelling is a break, a delay, a lingering, a moment which affords a distance between the elements and the I, and the I and its future. This opening, or space of recollection, is characterised by the gentleness and warmth of its intimacy, a warmth or gentleness which comes from the upsurge of another, who is the feminine being. By the feminine being Levinas quite explicitly does not mean the actual woman, nor to some supposed traditional role of woman. He speaks of the feminine in his analysis, as 'one of the cardinal points on the horizon in which the inner life takes place', and of the 'dimension of femininity' which remains open within the dwelling, as its very welcome.

Hospitality is, for Levinas, the very essence of the home. This does not mean that the home somehow fulfils its nature in receiving guests, but that its justification is not economic. It stands, potentially at least, as a concrete bearer of what Levinas called the responsibility to and for the other, a responsibility which falls on every one of us, which constitutes us as subjects, and from which we cannot escape.

The *Odyssey*

Homer's epic, the *Odyssey*, is concerned precisely with Odysseus' long return home from the Trojan War to Ithaca, where his wife and son wait for him. Joe Friedman, who was involved in the PA houses for many years, latterly at Shirland Road, has written of the usefulness of the *Odyssey* as a way of understanding what goes in the PA houses. In the houses, he writes,

> We do not just invoke homecoming metaphorically but literally also. We invite people to inhabit a home, which will not always be theirs but is theirs for the making. We invite them into an encounter that is not just metaphorical, in which the place of metaphor and the concrete (which in the form of 'practicality' is so often a defence against recognition) can be put into question. (Friedman, 2004: 29–30)

The *Odyssey* is, Friedman argues, centrally concerned with the idea of community – with questions such as 'what makes community possible', 'what does coming home mean' and 'what is the nature of hospitality'. Throughout the book Homer shows a deep concern with the nature of hospitality and the way we are given to judge the various characters and houses is through their extension – or not – of hospitality

Hospitality involves risk. The Greek word, *xeinos,* meaning both stranger and guest, guest-friend, embodies this tension. It seems extraordinary to us today that the guest/stranger was not required to introduce himself. The *Odyssey* shows the extremes of hospitality from the Kyklopes who kills many of Odysseus's companions and keeps him prisoner, to the Phaiakains, the first mortals Odysseus encounters in seven years and in whose company he is restored to himself. This is true hospitality. Friedman remarks that visitors to the PA houses are not required to speak or account for themselves until they feel ready to do so; they take their place in whatever is going on around them, the ordinary life of the house:

> An awareness of the complexity of hospitality is part of what the households hope to cultivate. One of the things that seems to be very difficult for people to get hold of is the way that hospitality involves obligations on both sides – because seeing this would involve a deconstruction of the notion of resident as innocent victim.(Friedman, 2004: 22)

Friedman also raises the question of what he calls 'the heroic', the stories that people tell themselves – and others – of their past glories and how hard this is to give up.

> Some of the heroic roles one encounters in community (and individual) therapy are 'the one who attempts to (re) institute justice by punishing the parents for something for which they should feel guilty', 'the adopted one who makes the natural family feel more together', 'the one who saves the family by satisfying the father's sexual appetites'. These heroic roles have come to define our residents' images of themselves and, like Odysseus, our residents resist giving up these socially-established places. The clinging to the heroic possibilities of

early childhood is also a holding on to a world where there are clearly recognisable heroes and villains, certainty regarding what is right and wrong. (ibid. p. 25).

As to the place of the therapists, Friedman suggests they are like Odysseus tied to his mast listening to the Sirens:

> Bound to their chairs they are free to experience what has previously been experienced only by Odysseus. As the residents unconscious heroic visions play through the group, the therapists become subject to them as to the Sirens' songs. They can become aware of them; and can comment on their presence. In community therapy, where the Siren song can be very compelling it is helpful to have more than one therapist present, so that if one is seduced by a particular tune, the others can pull him back from the rocks. (p. 26)

Finally Friedman argues that the *Odyssey* has a profound understanding of the nature and temporality of the notion of recognition which is central to the therapeutic process. Penelope does not recognise her husband immediately on his return but is fearful of seeing an image she wishes for, of being taken in by her desire. Her genuine recognition takes time.

> Homer shows here that it is not so much a question of Penelope recognising Odysseus but, rather, one of bringing her hopes and expectations and her new reality into tune with her own experience. She is faced with a recognition that will change her world. (p. 29)

The plight of dwelling

The German philosopher Martin Heidegger, best known for his monumental work *Being and Time*, addresses the question of dwelling directly in his essay, 'Building Dwelling Thinking'

(Heidegger, 1971). Heidegger's thinking was particularly important to Robin Cooper who lived at Portland Road for a number of years and worked at Shirland Road for many more, and provided the framework for his doctoral thesis on the nature of dwelling and hospitality (Cooper, 1984) and his evocative article, 'Dwelling and the "therapeutic community"' in the first book of essays from the PA (Cooper, 1989).

Like Levinas, Heidegger regards dwelling as an achievement. He links dwelling etymologically to being, through the old German word *Bauer* meaning to dwell, to *ich bin*, I am:

> The way in which you are and I am, the manner in which we humans are on the earth is Buan, dwelling. To be a human being means to be on the earth as a mortal. It means to dwell. (Cooper, 1989: 33)

For Heidegger the real plight of dwelling does not lie merely in the lack of houses:

> On all sides we hear talk about the housing shortage, and with good reason. Nor is there just talk; there is action too. We try to fill the need by providing houses, planning the whole architectural enterprise. However hard and bitter, however hampering and threatening the lack of houses remains, the real plight of dwelling does not merely lie in lack of houses. The real plight of dwelling lies in this, that mortals ever search anew for the nature of dwelling, that they must ever learn to dwell. What if man's homelessness consists in this, that man does not think of the real plight of dwelling as the plight.

Heidegger refers to the 'plight of dwelling'. Yet he makes it clear that this plight is not the same as the 'housing shortage'; and that the construction of houses, however essential and indeed praiseworthy a work this may be, carries with it no assurance that this 'plight of dwelling' will be anyway lessened.

In today's housing shortage even this much is reassuring and to the good; residential buildings do indeed provide shelter; today's houses may even be well-planned, easy to keep, attractively cheap, open to air, light and sun, but – do the houses in themselves hold any guarantee that dwelling occurs in them?

Heidegger suggests that we may in some respects fail to realise what it means 'to dwell', since the provision of all the seeming requirements is not sufficient to ensure that 'dwelling' in fact takes place. Thus it is that man's plight – man's plight of dwelling – consists in his ever having 'to search anew' for the nature of dwelling. Ever searching anew is a restlessness. It is not content with what it has hitherto found, or perhaps what is found is simultaneously lost. If man is always searching anew for his dwelling, he has forgotten, or perhaps, forgets what it means to dwell. 'The plight of dwelling may be a form of forgetfulness. Man dwells forgetfully.' It follows, Cooper says, that learning to dwell may not consist at all in acquiring further skills or competences, but will rather take the form of recollection.

> How will this recollection come about? How do we recall what it is to dwell? If we are to give thought to dwelling, we must think in a fashion which befits dwelling or belongs with dwelling. Such a thinking *stays* with that which calls upon us to think, or moves us to think; It is a meditative thinking rather than a calculative thinking which, with eyes fixed upon results, strays and wanders from its source. Such a thinking may itself already be a dwelling, for 'dwelling itself is always a staying with things. (Cooper, 1989: 33)

This staying with, Cooper reminds us, is not merely a matter of being around things, any more than dwelling is a matter of being within a habitation.

Dwelling is also linked to lingering. In Heidegger's words 'a staying with things'. as it is to wandering: 'Our dwelling is not of our doing – it is of our being.' (p. 33)

Dwelling is both lingering and wandering: lingering and wandering belong within the unitariness of dwelling. Staying stays, wandering changes – in each case, the same. Lingering has time for wandering, staying safeguards wandering's extravagancies. Lingering protects wandering, wandering nourishes lingering. Lingering stays with the wandering, wandering prolongs the lingering, as Scheherazade in *The Thousand and One Nights* prolongs her life each night, for yet one more day, by telling her story. Wandering spins a yarn which staying remains to hear, to gather the threads.

It is in our nature to stay, to stand, to stand out, to remain where we are, to take a place, to hold our ground, to inhere, rest and shelter. It is in our nature at the same time to fall and fall out, to wander and stumble, to err, to lose the thread, become distracted, to surrender, let go, turn and return. Dwelling is the between of lingering and wandering, turning and returning, gathering and dispersing, coming and going, loving and leaving, that between from which the world is born. (Cooper, 1989: 41–2)

The PA households, Cooper believed, provided 'the foremost illustration of a place of dwelling, a place where people dwell, where they unpack and get on with it It is made up of the people who live there, with one another, where living is the way "we go on being".' Any difference between such a house and another in the street is not be spelled out in terms of techniques and methods but rather 'in terms of its style, its way, its openness to the issues which arise in the course of its members living together and coming to acknowledge what they mean to one another' (Cooper, 1989: 46).

Intimate space

Finally I want to mention the philosopher Gaston Bachelard, who invented what he called topoanalysis – 'the systematic psychological study of the sites of our intimate lives' – as an auxiliary to psychoanalysis. For Bachelard the house is nothing less than 'one of the greatest powers of integration for the thoughts, memories and dreams of mankind'. Without the house, man would be 'a dispersed being'. The house maintains him through the storms of the heavens and through those of life. It is body and soul. It is the human being's first world. Before he is 'cast into the world', as claimed by certain hasty metaphysicians, man is laid in the 'cradle of the house.' (Bachelard, 1958: 6) Furthermore, Bachelard insisted, all space, if it is 'really-inhabited' bears 'the essence of the notion of home' (p. 5).

Dwelling, for Bachelard, is inseparable from the ability to dream. The house is a place in which day-dreaming is possible: The house we were born in is more than the embodiment of home, it is also 'an embodiment of dreams' (Bachelard, 1958: 15).

Whatever else they may be, the PA houses can be places also of day-dreaming, where such dreaming is allowed, where the dreamer is protected. They are one of those places which, in Bachelard's evocative phrase, 'invite us to come out of ourselves' (p. 11). The houses help one to say 'I will be an inhabitant of the world, in spite of the world.' (pp. 46–7).

CHAPTER 6

Ordinary Living:
The PA houses today

However they may have been theorised the PA houses have always aspired to be as *ordinary* as possible. This is something that goes back to Kingsley Hall which, Mary Barnes recalled many years later, was 'true to an ordinary way of living' (Barnes, 1989: 72). A casual visitor would sense little difference indeed from other shared houses. Residents have their own rooms in a large, well-appointed family house with a garden. They simply pay rent at a level coverable by housing benefit. They shop, cook and look after the house. They stay in their rooms, watch TV, go to the pub or the park.

How people come

People find their way to the houses in many different ways. A friend or relative may have suggested it, or a psychotherapist she is seeing, or a social worker. Some come through the Maytree, the sanctuary for the suicidal in north London. Others have heard of, or even read, RD Laing. In the past it was left to an interested person to approach the house directly, 'to make her own way', as it used to be said. She would have to make contact with the house and arrange to come to one of the house meetings. Each house usually had one designated meeting each week for visitors. For many this was a daunting prospect and, while it may well have been a test of an individual's desire to come to the house and her commitment to the idea, as was often said, it could also be something of a deterrent to all but the strongest-willed. Many people simply failed to make it to the house at all. And while it respected the place of existing residents and recognised that the house was their home which the new person wanted to join, it could also be very abused. People inquiring about a house were by no means guaranteed a warm welcome or even a welcome at all at some times. Too much was left to chance – that phone calls would be answered, that they would be dealt with sensitively, that any arrangement made by one resident would be communicated to others, that inquirers would not be put off unnecessarily.

Nowadays the house therapists have a first meeting with anyone who is interested. This is not an assessment of any kind, but a chance to see if the house is likely to be the right place for this particular person at this time. Some people do not have a real idea of what the houses are about, what moving in involves, and, when they learn, are not interested. Others may be looking for much more in the way of structured help than the houses offer. But if everyone feels it is right to do so, the person is invited to the house meeting for visitors. That she has met the house therapists makes it easier to come to a house of strangers but it is still a daunting prospect. The first meeting is an opportunity for people to get a sense of the particular house – what it looks like, where it is, what the household feels like, what it is like to sit in a meeting. The first meeting may well focus on the visitor who may be asked seemingly endless questions about who she is, where she has come from, what has brought her here, what has she done before, what she would like to do. Occasionally though a visitor will come into a meeting where what is going on in the house – tensions, difficulties, silences, conflicts among people – will be so present that there will be little space for her. Such a meeting, of course, may give a far more true picture of the actual house than one where people are on their best behaviour, at their most curious or seemingly interested.

If the visitor is still interested after this she will usually come back for three or four more meetings. In the past the process was more open-ended and decisions were often endlessly deferred, either by the house or the visitor. While it is true, as many said at the time, that this process of indecisiveness gave people a good idea of what it would be like to live in the house, too often it became an unhelpful way of being for both house and visitor. Many people simply dropped out, while others came to enjoy coming to meetings without making the crucial commitment to move in. At other times the process can be openly abused as we saw at Freegrove Road where a powerful group of residents made it impossible by their hostility for new people to come in.

It is not that residents have a veto on new residents. We are only too aware that people can tend to choose, even very subtly, people like themselves. What happens in the process of meeting and choosing new residents is truly democratic, not the limited democracy of votes, but a more profound democracy of genuine conversation and respect for people's views. Everyone has his or her say.

In this process residents – and therapists – inevitably come up against their own prejudices and the way in which we can all put onto others what we fear in ourselves, the projections that are part of everyday life. Visitors always touch things in ourselves that we find difficult to acknowledge and accept.

This process is not quick and can be difficult for all concerned but it is another sign of how our houses take people seriously and respect their views. By the end we hope that people might have some sense at least of what they are moving into and the house has a better sense of who they might be accepting. This is not only right in principle; it is right too in practice as the residents are the people who will have to live with the new person and if a mistake is made they will have to live with the consequences.

We sometimes say that moving into one of the PA houses involves a leap of faith. And in the end many people are simply unable to make this. It is too much to give up what they have, especially if they have established a home of their own already. Even if they do not have a home, the prospect of opening up old established ways of being and coping seems too much, even if these are not really working. There can be a real sadness here for many people as residents – and therapists – can become fond of and attached to particular individuals who then disappear from their lives.

Our houses do not work for everyone and we certainly do not accept everyone. Those who have a history of violence and those with a current (or very recent) dependence on alcohol or drugs are unlikely to be accepted. Hard-won experience has shown us that they are unlikely to benefit from our houses and unlikely too to be able to contribute much to the life of the community. As we saw the acceptance of people with serious drink problems caused great difficulties at Freegrove Road and has done so in other houses too.

This admission process is, however, just one small part of a person's entry into the house. It is just the beginning of the beginning. People make a grave mistake in thinking they just have to move their possessions into their room in order to settle in. It can be a real shock for a new resident to move in and then find the house empty, or that everyone is in their rooms. The community that existed during the meetings and that seemed to offer so much has vanished. The hoped for 'supportive' environment may be one person who offers to make a cup of tea. It is not surprising that the new resident herself ends up spending substantial periods of time away from the house, returning to the parental home for instance, or staying with friends. In these circumstance, we notice as Joe Friedman remarks, the new resident frequently turns to the house therapists who become idealised, at least they listen, and fellow residents are written off, at least for the time being (Friedman, 2004: 27).

Another scenario, not uncommon, is where an existing resident takes the new person under her wing, helps her move her things in, to unpack and make her room homely, goes with her to the local benefit office to get the necessary form, listens to her a lot, offers a great deal of 'care' and 'support', only to drop her when, sooner or later, she becomes 'too much', is too demanding.

Of course, there can also be a real welcome too, a genuine help that lasts beyond a day or a week or even a month.

Sooner or later the new resident comes to realise that what the house offers is not some artificial and inauthentic care and support but something a lot more complicated and, ultimately, more valuable.

Who comes?

There has always been a demand for the houses. Even though particular houses may have had low occupancy at times, sometimes to the point where their existence has been in question, ultimately they have survived because people have wanted to live there. There are, in any case, many reasons why a house may be low in occupancy for a time – the existing residents may be having a difficult time in themselves and find it difficult to accept new people or to be particularly open and welcoming to them; the house may have been full and word gets around that there are no spaces there. It takes time for word to get around that there are spaces once more. Because people can stay as long as they wish in the houses it is impossible to predict when someone may be leaving and so it is impossible to operate anything like a waiting list. We can and do contact people who have been in touch but most inevitably have found some other form of help.

But there is also something about the nature of the houses that means that they cannot be full all the time, perhaps, after a particularly difficult person has finally left or when long-standing residents move on. The house then needs what we all call in everyday life, a breathing space, a time not to be too bothered about the future, for the community to gather itself a bit. (This, of course, goes very much against the grain of today's ubiquitous 'performance indicators' and the like. A house with vacancies, it is claimed, is either not needed or not meeting the demand.)

In terms of who comes to the houses it is a sad fact that the PA has kept no records at all, of the people who have been in the houses, for 30 years. So it is impossible even to know with any accuracy the number of people who have been through our houses, let alone who they were and what brought them there and what happened when they left.

It is significant that this was not always the case. The early PA, surprisingly to many of us who have been accustomed to the PA's scepticism about such things, kept detailed information on those who came to Kingsley Hall and the communities which followed, who they were, their ages, how long they stayed, whether they were hospitalised during their stay, and so on. It did so because it saw quite clearly from the start that there was a very serious argument going on in the field of psychiatry. In challenging the orthodoxy the PA had to show that there were other ways of helping people who were severely distressed, that people wanted to come, that what it was doing was making a difference to those who came to it. The stakes were high.

By the late 1970s, however, this had stopped. Perhaps a complacency had set in. Or a scepticism, understandable but misguided, about the value of such information. (Laing himself was, as we saw in Chapter 2, pretty sceptical of the statistics he was forced to quote.) This was not, it might be said, just a matter of a lack of resources. The early PA was very poor indeed and while there have indeed been times when the houses have had to run on a shoestring, to the point where, when times were really bad, those responsible for them were not even paid, it is equally true that there have been times when the houses were relatively well-off and could easily have afforded to pay someone to do the kind of fairly minimal monitoring work necessary. The failing was much more to do with a shortsightedness on the part of those involved. Whatever the reasons, even if the PA was not interested in convincing others of the value of what it did, we have lost a part of our own history as a source of strength and inspiration and it cannot be replaced.

Diagnostic categories

As we saw in Chapter 1, the people involved in the early Philadelphia Association, Laing, Cooper and Esterson in particular, were primarily concerned with those people who had been designated psychotic, especially those labelled schizophrenic. And it is true, as we have seen, that the houses did see several people through acute psychotic episodes or 'freak-outs' as they were called. In addition the people in the PA houses who have been written about – Richard at Portland Road, Peter at Tollington Park (Oakley, 1989), as well as Mary Barnes at Kingsley Hall – would all fall under this heading.

It would be quite wrong however to think that this has been the sole or even the main point of the houses. (Just occasionally one senses disappointment on the part of visitors to house open days that there are no 'real psychotics' around, as in the old days.) The PA houses have always had room for people who would not be described as psychotic, those 'whose unfinished business took the form of the hard slog' (as the authors of the 'Beginnings' chapter in the first PA book put it (Cooper et al., 1989). There have always been in the houses the chronically depressed or the acutely anxious, people whose existence is just as tenuous and just as fearful as those designated psychotic. Indeed the houses probably only work if there is a mixture of people with different experiences.

The focus on the psychotic was in any case two-edged. While helping one person through extreme crisis it could also take a real toll on others who were not in the same sort of place and who were called on to help, sometimes for very lengthy and very demanding periods It also had the effect of taking attention away from those whose difficulties in life might be less dramatic and obvious but no less serious.

Labels, in any case, continue to mean as little to us as they did in the past and always carry the possibility of invalidation, of closing something down instead of opening it up. Our houses have always been open to people who want to live in them, regardless of any psychiatric or other diagnostic label they may have acquired. What matters is a wish to live in a particular house and a commitment to doing the emotional work that this involves. Many people who come to PA houses have had experience of psychiatric hospital; some have not. All have come to realise that their previous ways of coping have stopped working for them, if indeed they ever really did.

The house meetings

The main difference between the PA houses and other shared houses, of course, is that the people who live in them have particular experiences which have brought them there and in that the houses have a purpose. The purpose is to help people understand how they have come to be where they are and how, in time, they may come to take up a different place in relation to themselves and to others. This, in essence, is the work of the house and, in particular, of the meetings which take place in each house from three to five times a week depending on the circumstances of each house. The place and nature of the house meetings has changed considerably over time. Kingsley Hall had no regular meetings but members would convene when something needed to be sorted out or at meal times. The communities since have always had at least one regular meeting each week. Additional meetings might be called when needed, or they would just happen in response to a particular situation. But for some time our practice has been to have regular meetings at fixed times, usually for an hour and half, although there has been considerable variation between different houses. Shirland Road, for instance, had a meeting each day although one of these was designated an administrative meeting to deal with rent and other more practical matters; The Grove has four meetings and Freegrove Road has had three since it began, although this frequency has, in truth, had more to do with the economics of the house than any considered view of its needs.

The house meetings vary all the time, reflecting and expressing what is going on in the house. They are lively, flat, angry, anxious, engaged, bored, touching, and entirely unpredictable. One can never know beforehand how a meeting will be or what will take place in the course of it.

The meetings are the hub around which the houses revolve. Everyone is expected to attend and it is a condition of residents' tenancies that they do so. In practice, of course, it is very difficult to make people come to them; it is impossible to get people to do so in the right spirit. We hope that people come to see the usefulness of the meetings if they do not do so from the start and that they want to come and to make use of them, to join in the conversations of the house. The question of attendance at meetings can be an extremely tricky one for the house, especially the house therapists. We say we want people to take the time they need to find their way in the house and we say too that the houses should respect people's privacy and their need to be alone at times. If people are withdrawn surely this is one of the things they bring to the house, part of who they are. But at what point do we intervene and try to get people to meetings? What do we do if they do not? This is a question of judgment in the particular circumstances of each house and each resident. We are less worried about someone not coming to meetings if she is in touch with other people in the house, if they know she is alright and have a sense of what is going on with her. We are more concerned if a resident seems to be losing touch with the house altogether. Regular absences from meetings, of course, bring up things for those who do attend. Why are they 'getting away with it'? it may be asked. And of course it can lead others to think the meetings can be missed and that it is alright for them to miss them too. Staying away is also, of course, a way of being very present indeed as the meetings can – and do – focus on the one who is who absent and spend a great deal of time thinking about her.

Anything and everything to do with the life of the house and the lives of the people in it can be and is discussed here –

the difficulties people may be going through in themselves, how people are getting on with one another or not, who is doing (or more often not doing) the cleaning or the other household chores, the need for a new washing machine, and so on. What matters is not so much the *what* of the meetings but the *how*. People may well talk at length about what they feel but lack authenticity and real engagement with others. A sharp exchange about who makes the tea or cleans the bathrooms – and who never does – can be far more meaningful to the individuals concerned and to the house. Above all, the meetings are the places where people may try to speak to one another as truthfully as they can, both about themselves and about each other. In time people may feel freer in themselves and with others and better able to accept themselves and others.

The house meetings are not group therapy in any usual sense of the term. They are neither therapy of individuals in the context of the group – although many individuals try to make them this, taking up a lot of time and space to talk about themselves – nor are they therapy of the group. Our job is not to make interpretations about what is supposedly 'really going on' to which we have some privileged access. They are rather one of the ways in which we try to have a conversation and to make possible and encourage the community life of the house, to help the house be, and work as, a community, as opposed to a collection of individuals.

Individual therapy

In the past it was left entirely to individuals whether they wanted to be in their own therapy at all. Those who thought it helpful could do it, but no one was under any obligation to do so. Sometimes those who were in therapy would be seeing one of the house therapists, as happened at Portland Road where Hugh Crawford had several people in therapy at different times. So too, Haya Oakley wrote of her experience of seeing for therapy a young man in a house where she was also house therapist and the difficulties this could throw up (Oakley, 1989).

Nowadays we strongly encourage residents to be in their own individual therapy with someone not involved in the house, a recognition of the need for individuals to have their own space where they can explore what is private.

Some new residents will already be in therapy. Indeed, they may have come at the suggestion of their therapist. Others will come with little or no therapeutic experience. (We can usually find them therapists who will charge little money, usually students on the PA psychotherapy training.) Many embrace the opportunity, but others may be less willing. Reluctance and scepticism are to be respected, engaged with. Refusal, whether outright or dropping out soon after starting, can be signs of a hostility to the ethos of the house. In practice there is very little we can do in these situations other than argue and hope that people will see from the experience of others that this is something that might actually be helpful to them, not an imposition that they have to push against.

Does the existence of individual therapy alongside the house meetings lead to that state dreaded by therapists, 'splitting'? Clearly it can do and clearly it has done. People keep for therapy what should probably come to the house, and use the meetings to talk about things that would be better addressed in therapy. But on the whole the two seem to work well together, complementing each other for they are places quite different in nature. And while we respect the privacy of an individual's therapy, nowadays we would not refrain from talking to a therapist if we were particularly concerned about someone.

The place of the house therapists

As we have seen, the early PA communities, Kingsley Hall especially, but also the others which came after it, tried to break down the distinction between psychiatrist/psychotherapist and others who did not have this status. People were all in the house together. The idea was a worthy one. It recognised that people could be suffering and in distress regardless of any professional training or status. It also recognised that just because people had been subject to a psychiatric diagnosis did not mean they were not capable of responding to others in distress. This latter statement can be a surprising one for people unacquainted with our approach, so common is the belief that someone in the position of 'patient' is by definition unable to be involved with or helpful to others in distress. That our houses have challenged this notion, questioned the invalidation that psychiatric diagnoses too often bring, is one of the most important things we have done. Our houses have shown again and again and again that people have a remarkable capacity to respond, to engage with others, but that this has often been stifled by the definition, and experience, of being a patient. (How often is someone's lack of concern for others, his cut-offness, a result of the medication he has been taking for years?) When residents have gone into serious crises, for instance, it is remarkable how others seem to be able to step out of their own distress and to respond in ways that are authentic and imaginative. One of the tasks of the house therapists is to help the community function as a community, to help people mobilise their own resources as individuals and as a group. Of course, people can resist this and want to remain in the role of the patient, looking to the so-called experts for help. If we are called on the phone, for instance, by a resident our response is frequently to ask if she has talked about whatever is going on with someone else, others in the house. As often as not she has not done so, but we insist this is one of the most important things the houses are, places where people can talk to one another and help one another. Even this simple idea can go against the grain of current 'common sense' where people are discouraged from talking to others in a similar situation as though they are somehow unable to help or even understand or, worse, that their own suffering will be exacerbated by taking on the difficulties of others.

In practice, of course, it was never possible to abolish the distinction between therapists and others who were not, and the difference has become more formalised. Therapists (and those training to be therapists) no longer live in the houses or spend significant periods of the day there as once they might have done, almost as though they were their own, alternative, homes. Nowadays we are there only for meetings and when invited to a particular event, like a meal or party. The houses are the residents' homes, for the time being at least, and the therapists respect this. We do not use our keys to enter but ring the bell like any other visitor.

The early houses also were often run by one central figure. This came to an end with Hugh Crawford's death and the end of Portland Road where, it seemed clear to many, the final responsibility that lay with him had been too much for one person. More recently the houses have been run by groups of therapists, two, three, or even four as was the case at Shirland Road for a long time. These groups have been male and female, or both male or both female. There has never been an intention to replicate the 'parental couple'. The presence of more than one therapist is not just about sharing the burdens and responsibilities of running a house, although this is crucial. It also allows for a greater degree of freedom for both therapists who can take up different positions in relation to different residents and for residents who can relate differently over time to the different therapists. Having more than one therapist also means that therapists are less likely to get stuck in positions that are unhelpful but which they cannot see their way out of.

The actual ways in which house therapists take up their positions vary considerably and have as much to do with personal style and theoretical orientation as the ways of therapists seeing individuals. All the time we are responding to particular situations in specific houses with specific residents – or at least we try to. As with the ordinary therapist the position defies analogy, drawing on many different relationships – parent, friend, adviser – but covered by none. Our role may be closer to the original meaning of the Greek *therapeia* of one who waits upon or stands in attendance (see Friedman, 1989).

We are not experts, although many will look to us as though we are, looking directly to us for the 'answers' to their difficulties But we do have considerable experience, both individually and as a group of people who have been working in the houses for many years. We have a sense of what goes on in groups in general and in the houses in particular, the kinds of places that people can be put in by others, the roles assigned to them. Much of the time we are there to ensure fair play. We know something too of how difficult it is to move into the house and take up a place within it, and we know something too of the challenges of leaving. And we develop a sense of when individual residents and the group are being truthful about something or when they are avoiding difficult things. We are there, too, to encourage and to challenge, both individual residents and the house, to question for instance why the house seems opposed to someone new coming in when it feels depleted, to encourage people that they will be able to respond to the challenge, that they are far more resourceful than they believe themselves to be.

Our experience also allows us to weather the storms that inevitably beset the house. If the house is low in numbers and low in spirits we know that it has been here before and will, hopefully, come through. If there is serious conflict we know that it can pass, that the people who vow never to speak to each other again will, one day, be talking again, maybe even friends, or at least that the conflict can be lived with.

Nor are we figures of authority in the usual sense of the term, although again people, often newcomers, often those who have been in the psychiatric system, may treat us like that, seeking our permission to do things, for example to go away for a bit or to miss a meeting or to bring a pet to the house, or looking for approval. We cannot deny that we do have an authority – this would be a dangerous mystification – but this is a complicated authority that is all the time a matter of negotiation with others. We would never, for instance, impose a new resident on the house if others clearly did not want him. So too, although we can ultimately ask someone to leave if we consider he is a threat to the house or feel that she is not really making use of the house in a productive way, it is highly unlikely that we would do this if some residents, at least, did not share our view.

We can be, and often are, a focus of resentment. We do not have to live in the house, we do not have to put up with what others do. We come and go as we please, or so it seems. We have our nice homes and families, or so it can seem. So too can there be envy especially around times of the year that many find difficult, Christmas and summer. Robin Cooper once told of how, on his return from a family holiday in France, he brought two bottles of wine as a present for the house. One resident calmly took them from the table around which the meeting was gathered, opened them and poured the contents down the sink.

But this is only part of the story of how we are seen, how we are experienced. We can also be people who, if not to be emulated, at least show that different ways of being and living are possible. We can be seen as people who have had our own difficulties in life and who have found relationships, work and interests that matter to us.

However much we believe in a common humanity shared by residents and therapists, and however much we are aware of our own vulnerabilities and difficulties in life, and while casual observers of meetings might well not be able to make a clear distinction between residents and non-residents, there is always the inescapable fact that house therapists are doing a job, however privileged and fortunate we may feel in doing it. We get paid for what we do. In the end the responsibility for the houses lies with us. It is we who are responsible for making sure the house is full, as full as it can be, that there is enough money coming in to cover all the costs of running it, that the fabric of the building is maintained. Ultimately it is we who are responsible to the PA and to the outside world for the well-being of the residents.

RD Laing put the matter well, warning against fetishising the abolition of roles. Reflecting on Kingsley Hall and the early PA houses, he said,

> In our experimental places we've tried to do without roles. I'm not sure that doing without the roles really improves matters or is possible. That's not the essential of the thing. It's experimenting with social form so that we can find within the context of our social system the best sanctuary. (Evans, 1976: 89)

Using the house

There is no right way to be in the house. People use the houses in different ways. Some retreat as much as possible to their rooms, coming out to attend meetings or to make, almost surreptitiously, a cup of tea or something to eat in the kitchen when others are not around. Others make great efforts to establish some kind of community life. They make meals or organise others to do so, arrange a chores rota, attend to the maintenance that inevitably needs to be done in a large house and so on.

What are we to do though when, as happens, someone comes to the house but makes it clear he is not interested in getting into his own therapy or even attending the meetings, although he comes because he is 'supposed' to and knows that if he does not that his tenancy will be in question? This man is not openly aggressive to others. or disruptive. He pays his rent and may even do his share of the household tasks. This man is obviously getting something from being in the house, a pleasant physical environment, for instance, or companionship. Or in another scenario someone feels unable to be in the house and spends a great deal of time away, either at a friend's or parent's house, but does not want to give up her tenancy. It seems that these matters often turn on the question at what point does someone's particular way of being in the house become intolerable or unacceptable to others? At what point does someone's way of being in the house become anti-house? These (and many other) questions cannot be answered in the abstract but arise in a context of a particular individual in a particular household at a specific time. A house that is relatively full, reasonably vibrant, hopeful, will be able to tolerate such a presence more readily than a house which has a number of spaces and where energy and morale are low. Someone who is struggling to be in the house in a meaningful way will be tolerated more than someone who is taking the house for granted.

A time to heal

Time is absolutely central to what we do. Here there has never been a question of artificial time limits. People have always been able to stay for as long as they needed. This is not a matter of policy. It is part of our ethos. It would be absurd to say, as we do, to someone in severe distress or seriously dislocated, 'You can make this place your home but you must leave within six months or even two years.' There is simply no way of knowing how long it may take a person to work through what she has to work through. People who do not feel at home in themselves or the world can easily take this sort of time even to *begin to feel at home*. There are no short cuts to the time of moving in, settling in, being there, making oneself at home as much as one can. This bare fact, that there are no short cuts, is something that our culture finds hard to accept, so used have we become to deadlines and time limits. Time and time again people say it is this sense of not being pushed, of not being treated, that has made a difference. The gift of time is one of the most important things that we give to people who are suffering. Without it there would be nothing.

It is not that people *have* to stay for a long time to get what they want or need. People stay for various periods. It is rather that people have to know that they *can* stay as long as they want, that no one will be throwing them out after a certain, fairly arbitrary period. How long this is no one can possibly know in advance.

Here the houses can involve a certain playing for time. The longer someone stays the more at home she may become, the more at ease she may be, the less strange the whole business may seem. In the same way in the PA houses we very much hope that people will take their time – and be given time by others – to feel at ease, or at least less ill at ease, in their strange new environment.

The houses have implicitly recognised the truth of Levinas's insistence that time is not the achievement of an isolated subject but 'the very relationship of the subject to the Other'. Time *is* my relationship to others and theirs to me. We commonly say 'We have no time for X' thus consigning X to a category different to that in which we include our loved ones and our friends and even the acquaintances for whom we do have time.

This kind of time stands in contrast to more ordinary ideas of time, the time of appointments with a GP, with a psychiatrist, with other professionals, all of whom have very limited time indeed for their patients and clients. This is not to criticise the individuals concerned. The unavailability of time in these settings is not personal; it is structural. In our houses, as in therapy, time is one of the cornerstones of the endeavour.

While it has become more accepting of the reality of emotional suffering, our culture still finds it difficult to accept something that, in effect, challenges our normal attitude to time, the time of appointments, and meetings, and agendas and things to be done and achieved, and done as quickly as possible, the time of what is called 'productivity'. Sooner or later most people in the houses will encounter the statement from families, friends or others that they have had enough time, that they should be getting on with their lives. Often this means no more than getting some job that has no meaning other than as a means of survival. The houses have implicitly challenged the notion that any kind of work is better than doing nothing or 'idleness'.

But it is impossible to enforce this and counter to our belief about promoting autonomy. Time belongs to no one despite the attempts of governments and others to control what people do with it. We want people to come into their own desires and to follow those, not those imposed by others.

We may hope, we do hope, that people in the houses will come to accept the *responsibility* of time and use it wisely. We are alert, I think, to people getting stuck, can and do encourage people to do things if this seems desirable – to do some voluntary work, or take up a course of study or even just get out of the house more.

There is, it needs to be said, a very real practical problem in where people are supposed to go when they want to leave. At times in the past we have had the good fortune to be allowed to nominate people for housing association properties and this was hugely important to the individuals who benefited and to the houses which then had free spaces. But this has not been the case for some time and the absence of suitable rented accommodation in London is a very grave problem for us, as it is for everyone else. In addition there is the strange common assumption that what people really ought to aspire to is to live on their own so the provision of shared accommodation for adults is even worse. Residents in the houses spend years struggling to be part of a community only to face the prospect of having to live on their own as though this were some great achievement.

Being there

Outside of the meetings people are free to do as they please. They spend time in their rooms, go out. Some people study, some do voluntary work. They cook, they clean. Nothing is required. People who have grown up doing as they are told, acting in accordance with the desires of others do not need this from us, that they do what we think is best for them. One of the most difficult issues here is to do with the idea of work. The houses implicitly challenge, as they always have done, the notion that 'work' in itself is somehow 'good' for people, that 'doing something', however menial or mind-numbing is somehow better than 'doing nothing'. One of the residents at Kingsley Hall said to Morton Schatzman:

> ... I don't any more believe in the complicated mystique surrounding the necessity for work. I mean pointless and unfulfilling work ... I've discovered this here because here I find that many people question many things with a greater honesty. People with obvious honesty question many things that one has been taking to be unconditionally true and valid. (Schatzman, 1972: 200)

'What do you do?', is very often one of the question we ask someone we have just met, a question that does not just seek information but is too often a judgment of some kind. Many people come to the houses having done such work, sometimes for a long time, and they struggle endlessly with the idea that they are somehow lazy and worthless, because they are 'not working'. The social stigma attached to this state of 'not working' is as great as that of being seen as in some way 'mentally ill'.

Of course people can get stuck, doing nothing except watching TV but, again and again we see people get out of it by themselves, in time, often with the quiet encouragement of other residents who have been there before them. Our hope is that people, in their own time, come into their own desires and find work that is genuinely meaningful to them. As the resident just quoted also said, the retreat from social reality afforded by Kingsley Hall paradoxically made facing reality almost unavoidable (Schatzman, 1972: 200)

Friendships and relationships

People do, of course, form friendships with others in the house, although these may often shift over time. And people also do get into sexual relationships with others in the house although this is far from a frequent occurrence. What Robin Cooper remarked about Portland Road in this respect (see Chapter 3) holds true more generally. People who come to the houses find relationships with others very difficult and are not likely to be in a place for this most difficult and testing of relationships. Also, as Robin Cooper remarked, the atmosphere of the houses can be familial to an extent that it simply feels inappropriate to get involved sexually with another resident. But it does happen – it would be odd if it did not – but it is almost invariably problematic for the house when it does. As we saw the formation of two couples at Freegrove Road was a factor in stopping newcomers to the house at a time when it badly needed them. At other times houses have had to deal with all the ordinary feelings stirred up by the presence of sex – from discomfiture to jealousy and envy – and all the fallout of the end of such affairs, the anger, bitterness, resentment, disappointment and so on.

All that said two people did get together at Shirland Road and had a baby there who lived as contented a life as many until the house was forced to close. The presence of such a young child, it might be added, shocked the inspection team who carried out the Supporting People review. Long gone were the days when such a child might be thought lucky to have the attention and company of so many people in addition to his parents.

Leavings and endings

People leave the houses for all sorts of reasons and in all sorts of ways. Some, disappointed that the house is not what they had imagined, drift away, spending less and less time at the house, and more with family or friends.

People also leave, of course, when they are more ready to do so, when they feel they have exhausted the possibilities of the house. Ideal or perfect departures are rare. Even when a leaving or ending is planned, the challenge of leaving and all that it brings can be too much. Not infrequently we see individuals get into a position of opposition to the house or anger in order to avoid what can be very difficult feelings of loss – of a home, of a community, of a way of living – and gratitude.

While some people do keep in touch with the house once they have left, usually if they have been close friends with another particular resident, most people seem to want to get on with their new lives and, sooner or later, lose contact with the house. Others do stay part of the loose network of the PA and some residents have gone on to be therapists themselves.

A very different kind of leaving was forced on a whole house by the closure of Shirland Road in 2006 described in Chapter 2. Here, for more than a year, the house which was full with nine residents had to face the inevitable, however much people might have fled into fantasies of a rescue. In the end everyone in the house was found other accommodation, invariably on their own, but it was the end of a community that had lasted for many years and a real trauma for all those involved and for the PA.[1]

Do they work?

The PA houses do not fit easily into the current obsession with 'evidence-based practice'. It is not that there is no evidence of whether the houses work or not. There is plenty but it is not of the kind that appeals to people who think that what cannot be

1. See the paper by Marie-Laure Davenport, 'A home is broken' on the PA website: www.philadelphia-association.co.uk.

measured is somehow irrelevant. As former house therapist Christina Moutsou says:

> We live in a culture that seeks concrete evidence of progress and achievement. Evidence often entails a fixed notion of what a well person is supposed to be like. The PA houses invite people to think about their own lives and histories and about how they want their lives to be as opposed to how they are expected to be. (Moutsou, 2008: 71)

What we do have though is the collective memories of those who have been involved in the houses over the years. We know of the people whose lives were saved by spending time in the houses or whose lives the houses helped to turn around, of the people who have been able to come off, or significantly reduce, their medication or their dependence on psychiatric services, of the people who have been able to find meaningful work or education and make meaningful relationships. These are not things easily measured by any standard forms or research 'instruments'.

When our Shirland Road house was facing closure in 2006 seeveral residents and ex-residents wrote movingly of their lives before they found their way to the house and after. They spoke of the 'revolving door' syndrome familiar to all in the field – of breakdown, followed by admission to psychiatric hospital, followed by discharge, followed by re-admission – of being in states of isolation and despair and of finding in the close haven, a place of acceptance, a place to be ordinary. One resident, Melanie, wrote:

> Before entering the house my life was extremely limited and I saw no hope of changing things. I was living alone in a bedsit with no job and no friends. All my energy was devoted to making sure I ate enough to stay out of hospital. I had spent many years in and out of hospital for anorexia. I had great difficulty interacting with people in a healthy way which

resulted in me not being able to hold down a job or form any meaningful friendships. A relationship was out of the question. I was simply surviving not living and felt that I could not continue in this way for much longer. My therapist told me about the PA community and it seemed my only hope … In the house, for the first time in my life, I found a place that felt like home and a group of people with whom I belonged. The experiences, were, I felt, deeply important in enabling me to grow and were the template which I could then extend to the world outside.

It is clear that being in a PA house makes returning to psychiatric hospital (or involvement with other mental health services a lot less likely. This is obviously better for the individual concerned, but it also saves a huge amount of public money. At the time of writing, people pay rent of around £120 each week. This compares with an estimated cost of £2,600–£3,100 to keep someone in a psychiatric hospital for the same period, or costs of £6–800 for conventional supported housing

Therapeutic communities?

Although we have often in the past used the term 'therapeutic communities' to describe our houses, the reality is that we differ in many respects from such entities, so much so that we now avoid the term, preferring the slightly more awkward and less familiar 'community households' to describe what we do.

The primary way in which we differ from the usual 'therapeutic community' is that such places invariably seek to *treat* people in some way and have a structure and rules and procedures in place to carry this out. The typical therapeutic community has a structured day – meals, group meetings, household activities such as cleaning, shopping and cooking, forms of therapy such as art, movement, dance and so on. We are not denying that all houses need the cooperation of those

living there if they are to work, if they are not to descend into
at best mess and dirt and at worst chaos. Nor are we denying
that individuals can benefit hugely from different forms of
therapeutic help. We have no argument with such statements.
Where we disagree with other approaches is that we believe
that more is to be gained by letting the house and its members
deal with these matters, that something is lost if people are
treated as if they are children or adolescents. While recognising
individual vulnerabilities and differences in capabilities, our
houses try to treat people as responsible adults who are capable
of sorting out these sorts of things for themselves. A shared
meal, for instance, is far more meaningful if it happens because
some people want it to and do what needs to be done to make
it happen, than if it is the result of an instruction or even wish
on the part of others not living in the house. John Heaton
recalls how filthy Ascott Farm was but when one of the women
living there got pregnant and said she wished to have her baby
born in the house, the other residents cleaned the whole house,
especially the area near the room chosen for the delivery
(Heaton, 2005).

　　We are not interested in the inculcation of what are
sometimes called social skills or encouraging social learning.
What such approaches do, as Joe Friedman has argued, is to
abstract from the fabric of community 'functions' which are
seen as having some therapeutic potential. But this is to see
only 'the husk of community'.

　　For though community like play does involve an intricate
　　structure of rules and regulations which are instantly in play
　　it is precisely *how* this structure exists for someone that
　　determines their potential involvement in it. It is this 'how'
　　that an individual plays out in his involvement (or lack of it)
　　in the world. It is his throw into the game. Therapy involves
　　taking up this throw as the opening throw of a game, an
　　invitation to play. To regard this throw as a misthrow, to be
　　corrected by training in social skills, is not only a refusal of a

particular and personal invitation to play (however disguised and unconscious) but a presentation of community as mechanical. (Friedman 1989: 66–7)

In addition, therapeutic communities adhere implicitly, if not explicitly, to a clear, sometimes rigid, distinction between 'patients' (however they may be designated in a particular place) and staff. As we have seen, from the outset the PA has tried to put this distinction into question, although we have to recognise that experience has shown that such distinctions are not easily done away with, to put it mildly.

Furthermore while we have been members, albeit inconsistently, for many years of the Association of Therapeutic Communities, the increasing professionalisation of the field, with all its auditing and validation process begun under the name of 'Community of Communities', was something which seemed to us to take the 'movement' further and further into the area of the technical, a place from which we wish to distance ourselves entirely. The search for 'professionalism' and status recognition which have spurred these developments are taking it more and more into what Robin Cooper called 'the collective institution of voluntary servitude' (Cooper, 2001: 525). It is not that we are somehow 'against standards', but the laying down of criteria against which almost every aspect of 'community' life is to be measured, is fatal to the life and spirit of what we (and doubtless others) are about.

In the end perhaps the matter is really quite simple. We are not interested in the applications of technique or the deployment of supposed technical expertise on the part of the therapists. We are not involved in showing people the way, however benevolently this might be done. Our practice is – as it always has been – about helping people find their own way, rooted in all the difficulties of ordinary living.

CHAPTER 7

Against All Odds:
Some concluding remarks

Like other radical organisations of the period, the Philadelphia Association has had to adapt to times completely different to those which prevailed when it came into existence. As we saw in Chapter 1, the PA, in questioning mainstream psychiatry both in its thinking and treatment, was very much part of the radical movements of the 1960s which challenged long-established ways of seeing and doing things and which put in question many forms of traditional authority, for example between blacks and whites in the USA, South Africa and in Britain; between women and men, the treatment of gays and lesbians and so on. These movements failed in their larger objectives. Capitalism, imperialism and patriarchy were not overthrown as many had hoped and repressive regimes the world over were not toppled. The Prague Spring of 'socialism with a human face' was crushed by Soviet tanks; the involvement of the United States in Vietnam escalated considerably and only ended in the 1970s, by which time much of the country was a waste land; apartheid was eventually overthrown but only after more than 20 years of suffering and struggle. In the United Kingdom the 1970s began symbolically with the trial of people involved with the alternative magazine *Oz*. Although they were acquitted by a jury, the charge brought against them – that they had conspired to corrupt public morals – was extremely serious and could have brought them long prison sentences. (As it was the three accused were actually held in prison for a brief time during which they were forced to submit to the symbolic humiliation of having their hair cut.) More important, and not just symbolically, was the election in 1970 of a government of the right under Edward Heath, although it would be another nine years before the election of a government (under Margaret Thatcher) even more to the right and one explicitly dedicated to the complete eradication of what it saw as the insidious legacies of the Sixties.

Nevertheless these movements did achieve a great deal; they changed the nature of politics. Inequalities and inequities were not abolished but they could no longer be taken for granted and even if it took them years to address, governments had to acknowledge this. The civil rights legislation in the US, the anti-discrimination laws in the UK, the recognition of the rights of gays and lesbians and so on – none of these would have happened without the radical political movements of the Sixties. In the field of 'mental health', the rights and interests of psychiatric patients have come to be articulated far more powerfully, whether through groups such as MIND or the critical psychiatry network or the very vocal 'users' movement, than they ever were in the past. The PA can take some credit for this in its insistence that the voices of those designated 'mentally ill' should be listened to as much as those of others. Assessing the legacy of RD Laing, Zbgniew Kotowicz puts it well: 'Laing was one of those who gave the mentally ill, the patients, the "psychiatrised" a voice. The force and imagination of his plea helped the sufferers speak out. Perhaps this is Laing's most tangible legacy.' (Kotowicz, 1997: 119) This is something the PA – and many others – has continued to insist on.

In running its houses, the PA has had to deal, not just with threats from outside, from bureaucracies which cared little for what we were about, or from the challenging and sometimes destructive behaviour of residents. It has also had to face difficulties *within* the organisation, arising from the inevitable differences of interest and approach. Any honest account of the PA households has to recognise this.

From the start there were always tensions over the houses and how they should be run. David Cooper, while one of the founding members of the PA and one of its inspiring figures, seems to have been little interested in the idea at all – according to Laing he did not even visit Kingsley Hall. Cooper's particular understanding of politics, and the place of what was called mental illness in it, would take him to an identification with urban guerrilla movements, such as those in Latin America, and a more 'political/mystical' form of writing. At Kingsley Hall there were tensions between those who still saw a need for a medical authority, as did Aaron Esterson, and those who wished to see such distinctions done away with. Since Kingsley Hall there have been differences in approach between those who have leaned more towards the provision of asylum and those whose emphasis has been on dwelling, those who have favoured more of a structure to the houses and those who thought there should be less, and differences too about the place of therapy in the houses.

Much of the time the PA was able to deal with such differences, although it is significant that both Cooper and Esterson were to leave the PA soon after Kingsley Hall closed. Different houses, as we have seen, had different emphases and inflections, depending on who was involved in them. Indeed this is something that continues to this day. At other times the houses have posed a more serious problem for the organisation.

Since the early 1980s, and particularly since the death of Hugh Crawford and the closure of Portland Road, the houses became more and more separate from the rest of the PA. While under the auspices of the PA, constitutionally the houses had always been entities separate from it, responsible to their own management committees and for running their own affairs, including setting budgets and establishing their own ways of working. Differences of approach and the interpersonal difficulties that are an inevitable part of any organisation meant that it became increasingly difficult to recruit PA members to the committees set up to manage the houses. It should also be said that many PA people were simply not interested in getting to grips with the rapidly changing face of social housing and welfare benefits which inevitably affected the houses. (This, it might be said, was perfectly understandable. People in the PA are, first and foremost psychotherapists. We are not housing workers.) It was left to a few individuals to deal with such matters. This autonomy then allowed critics to claim the houses were unaccountable and those who had developed some expertise in housing or welfare regulation were, rather unfairly, blamed for misusing their power.

This coincided with changes in the culture of the PA in a wider sense. There were fewer parties and other events that might bring people from the houses together with others from the network. The PA became less of a community. So too the development of the PA Study Programme of talks and seminars, into the more formal Introductory Course closed off another place of meeting. Residents – and others – had always been welcome to attend those parts of the Study Programme in which they were especially interested, while the Introductory Course (for good reasons of its own) required a commitment for regular attendance for a year.

For their part the house therapists often felt that they were left to carry the burdens of the houses with little interest or support from colleagues. The PA, it seemed to them, was happy to take the credit for the houses but did not want to know about the hard work that went into running them day by day, week by week, over many, many years. These burdens, as we have seen, have ranged from worrying about the future of a particular house when occupancy was low, not getting paid when there were few residents, dealing with serious crises, people 'freaking out', attempted suicide and, fortunately rare, actual suicide, threats of personal violence and so on. The days had long passed when a house could call on the PA 'network' to help deal with a crisis. House therapists were left pretty much to their own resources – and those of the houses – to deal with such occurrences. Hilary Cooper recalled that when she and other people on the PA training took over the Grove in the early 1980s when the previous therapist had left, there was only one resident, 'No rent had been collected for months and there was no money to pay us. That was the case for several years. We would go to meetings with this one resident who would be sitting surrounded by empty beer cans in a house that no one would have wanted to live in.' (Fortunately this man was shortly rehoused and a new group brought together to live in the house but it still took many years to turn the house around.) Over the years several people who had worked in the houses would either leave the PA altogether or remain members but at a distance, feeling their work for it had not been appreciated.

Although house therapists were sometimes accused of having created jobs for life, when spaces did open up for new therapists there was very little interest indeed from the vast majority of members. It is probably true to say that it was not so much that people wanted to be house therapists – clearly most did not – but that being a house therapist was the only way in which PA members could earn money as therapists from the PA. At a time when regular therapeutic work seemed harder and harder to get, this became a source of resentment. (House therapists it should be added, have never been well paid, certainly not given the responsibilities involved, and as self employed, have never benefited from the ordinary employment rights enjoyed by most people.)

Strangely, for an organisation that would often refer to its houses as one of the things that made it different from others in the world of psychotherapy, the houses played no part at all in the PA psychotherapy training for many years. A current colleague claimed not even to know of the existence of the PA houses until well into his training. Trainees who did enquire about getting involved were usually told that they, like the residents, had to 'find their own way'. One colleague who tried to do so and rang one of the houses to open up a conversation about how he might get involved was told in no uncertain terms to get lost.

If the PA had lost touch with its houses, the houses had also lost any sense of belonging to something bigger than themselves, the PA network. Houses seemed to exist as individual entities with little or no contact among them or with the wider PA. But this separation was not the 'fault' of those involved in the houses, far less the result of some plan. It was rather something that had happened and had been allowed to happen. It was the houses which undoubtedly suffered in these circumstances, unable to rely on the interest or support of the wider network.

To its credit the PA has, in recent years, addressed this gap between the houses and the rest of the organisation. For some years now people training with the PA have been required to be involved with one of the houses for several months during their training, usually by attending one of the house meetings and by being around in the house at some other time. (Two former students, Christina Moutsou and Jake Osborne, who did such placements went on to become house therapists.) The houses put on open days for the PA network and residents come to some PA public events, something that had not really happened for a long time. Most important perhaps, there are many more conversations in the organisation about what the houses are doing, their ideas and practices, and the difficulties they face, than there have been in a very long time.

In the end we have survived when many others have not or have done so only at the price of changing significantly what they stood for. While the houses moved from being run by – and identified with – charismatic, male figures, with a very explicit philosophical standpoint, to something more shared and more ordinary, they have not lost their idealism. It is just that this is less to the foreground. What we stand for today, remains essentially the same as what the PA stood for when Sid Briskin, Aaron Esterson, RD Laing and others took over Kingsley Hall that weekend in June more than 40 years ago. This is above all an idea of respect for the person against all the odds of the age and a belief that 'mental illness', emotional suffering, psychological distress, call it what you will, can, in time and with patience, be made sense of and, more important, worked through.

'What do you do when you don't know what to do?'. This question posed by RD Laing on many occasions, continues to confront us, a question that cannot be answered by any recourse to techniques, however well-intentioned they might be. It is one of the hardest things to let things be, to let people be. This was very clear in the case of Richard at Portland Road (Chapter 3) but it has been shown many times since in less extreme cases. To walk the line between what Leon Redler many years ago called 'indifferent neglect' or 'ignorant, intrusive interference' is a matter of considerable complexity and difficulty.

And we continue to affirm the idea of community despite the devaluation of the idea in everyday discourse. A 'warmly persuasive word', Raymond Williams noted in *Keywords* (Williams, 1983), it seems never to be used unfavourably. No one can be against it. Everything, from care to policing, must carry the epithet, as though to emphasise its true absence, a sort of official wishful thinking. Yet for us it remains an important ideal, not something fixed but something dynamic, not something in existence but something always in the making, something to be struggled for, which arrives, if it does, almost unnoticed and through which people may find a more meaningful place in the world.

In the PA building is a memorial stone to our friend and colleague Robin Cooper. It bears the words that Robin liked from Samuel Beckett's *Malone Dies*:

A bright light is not necessary, a taper is all that one needs to live in strangeness if it faithfully burns.

The burning taper is, in our case, not merely symbolic. It is real and has been to the benefit of the hundreds of people who have spent time in our houses over the years and whose lives were occasionally saved, more often significantly changed, through the experience of being there.

References

Asylum, Peter Robinson, 1972 (DVD).

Bachelard, G (1958) *The Poetics of Space* (trans. Maria Jolas). Boston, MA: Beacon Press.

Barnes, M & Berke, J (1971) Mary Barnes: Two accounts of a journey through madness. London: MacGibbon & Kee. (Also New York: Other Press, 2002 with new material by Joseph Berke.)

Barnes, M with Scott, A (1989) *Something Sacred: Conversations, writings, paintings*. London: Free Association Books.

Berke, J, Masoliver, CP & Ryan, TJ (1995) *Sanctuary: The Arbours experience of alternative community care*. London: Process Press.

Cooper, D (1967) *Psychiatry and Anti-Psychiatry*. London: Tavistock.

Cooper, D (ed.) (1968) *The Dialectics of Liberation*. Harmondsworth: Penguin.

Cooper, R (1984) Dwelling and hospitality: A phenomenological inquiry into therapeutic community. PhD Thesis.

Cooper, R, et al. (1989) *Thresholds Between Philosophy and Psychoanalysis: Papers from the Philadelphia Association*. London: Free Association Books.

Cooper, R (1989) Dwelling and the 'therapeutic community'. In Cooper et al., pp 31–55.

Cooper, R (1996) What we take for granted. *Free Associations, 40*, 530–50.

Cooper, R (2000) The state we're in. *Free Associations, 47*, 507–29.

Deleuze, G & Guattari, F (1977) *Anti-Oedipus: Capitalism and schizophrenia*, (trans. R Hurley, M Seem, HR Lane). Minneapolis: University of Minnesota Press.

Evans, RJ (1976) *RD Laing: The man and his ideas*. New York: EP Dutton.

Family Life, Ken Loach, 1971 (DVD).

Friedman, J (1989) *Therapeia*, play and the therapeutic household. In Cooper et al., pp. 56-75.

Friedman, J (2004) The *Odyssey*, community and therapy. In P Gordon & R Mayo (eds), *Between Psychotherapy and Philosophy: Essays from the Philadelphia Association* (pp. 17–30). London: Whurr.

Guattari, F (1996) Mary Barnes's 'Trip'. In G Genosko (ed.) *The Guattari Reader* (pp. 46–54). London: Blackwell.

Heaton, J (2005) The early history and ideas of the Philadelphia Association. Paper presented to the Critical Psychiatry section of the Royal College of Psychiatry, Edinburgh.

Heidegger, M (1971) Building, dwelling, thinking. In *Poetry, Language, Thought* (pp. 143–61), (trans. Albert Hofstadter). London: Harper and Row.

Heller, A (1995) Where are we at home? *Thesis Eleven, 41,* 1–18

Hickey, B (2008): Lothlorien community: A holistic approach to recovery from mental health problems. *Therapeutic Communities, 29*(3): 261–72.

Kotowicz, Z (1997) *RD Laing and the Paths of Anti-Psychiatry.* London: Routledge.

Laing, RD (1985) *Wisdom, Madness and Folly: The making of a psychiatrist.* London: MacMillan.

Laing, RD (1972) Metanoia: Some experiences at Kingsley Hall, London. In HM Ruitenbeek (ed.), *Going Crazy: The radical therapy of RD Laing and others.* New York: Bantam.

Laing, RD & Esterson, A (1964) *Sanity, Madness and the Family: Families of schizophrenics.* London: Tavistock. (Second edn. Pelican Books, 1970.)

Levinas, E (1969) *Totality and Infinity: An essay on exteriority* (trans. Alphonso Lingis). Pittsburgh: Duquesne University Press.

Moutsou, C (2008) When philosophy meets practice: Setting up a Philadelphia Association community household. In J Gale, A Realpe & E Pedriali (eds) *Therapeutic Communities for Psychosis* (pp. 63–72). London: Routledge.

Mullan, R (1995) *Mad to be Normal: Conversations with RD Laing.* London: Free Association Books.

Mullan, R (ed.) (1997) *RD Laing: Creative destroyer.* London: Cassel.

Oakley, H (1989) Touching and being touched: The negotiated boundaries and the 'extended' consulting room. In Cooper et al., pp. 146–66.

Rowbotham, S (1973) *Women's Consciousness, Man's World.* Harmondsworth: Penguin.

Schatzman, M (1972) Madness and morals. In R Boyers & R Orrill (eds) *Laing and Anti-Psychiatry* (pp. 181–208). Harmondsworth: Penguin.

Showalter, E (1987) *The Female Malady: Women, madness and English culture, 1830–1980*. London: Virago.

Sigal, C (2005) *Zone of the Interior*. Hebden Bridge: Pomona.

Szasz, TA (1976) Anti-psychiatry: The paradigm of the plundered mind. *The New Review*, *3*(29), 2–12 .

Williams, R (1983) *Keywords: A vocabulary of culture and society*. London: Fontana.

An Uneasy Dwelling

Appendix 1:
PA communities*

Kingsley Hall, 1965–1970

Archway, 1970–1978/1979

Portland Road, 1971–1980

The Grove, 1972 – still going

Tollington Park, 1973–1978

De Beauvoir Square, 1974–1978

Ascott Farm, Stadhampton, 1977–1988

Mayfield Road, 1978–1982

Bradley Gardens, 1982–1985

Holland Road, late 1970s to early1980s

Shirland Road, 1983–2006

Maygrove Road, 1983–1990

Freegrove Road, 1996– still going

---

* An incomplete list

Appendix 2:
Reviews of *Asylum*

The critics were divided. George Melly in the *Observer* said it had 'a feeling of almost smug omnipotence'. It was not entirely convincing and begged too many questions. Nevertheless he urged anyone interested 'in the problem of alienation and its causal links with our society' to see it (3 September 1973). In the *Guardian* (5 October), Derek Malcolm thought 'as a piece of film it is not much' – a view shared by the *New Statesman's* John Coleman who concluded 'what a lot of technical know-how the new breakaway film-makers still have to catch up on'. But Malcolm continued:

> If you want to think it will certainly make you, being provoking, moving, irritating, voyeuristic and totally compulsive at one and the same time. it could well be supremely important for the future of mental treatment. (27 September)

Writing at greater length in *The Times*, David Robinson said the opposite, concluding that this 'extraordinary' film made us feel that we were 'more aware of looking in a mirror than watching a voyeuristic succession of case histories'. Director Robinson and his team, he said, had not observed or documented or depicted so much as participated in the venture, slipping in and out of the picture, taking their part in 'the interminable chatter and debate that are central to the life of the place'. This was no 'propaganda piece' for the ideas of RD Laing. The camera 'simply wanders around and watches and participles with the same gentle curiosity that he himself displays in discussion with the inmates' (5 October).

In the *Financial Times* Nigel Andrew said it was one of
those rare films that deserved and demanded to be seen twice.
Any sense of voyeurism was he said 'vitiated here by the
complete frankness of the participants, as they talk, quarrel, or
fight their problems through' and by the involvement of the
crew who slip in and out of the frame. The film was 'a clear
vindication' of Laing's belief in 'the viability of a personal rather
than a clinical relationship' between psychotherapist and patient
(28 September).

In the *New York Times* Roger Greenspan described it as
'enterprising but humanly decent', a film which did not exploit
but 'explored' the difficulties it portrayed (30 September) and
Howard Smith in the *Village Voice* said it was 'beautifully done'
(no date). The critic of the *Toronto Globe and Mail*, Martin
Knelman, said the film was 'almost terrifyingly involving'. Rarely
had a movie screening seemed 'such an important intellectual
event' (31 March).

Index

Index

The Hope of Therapy

Paul Gordon

ISBN 978 1 906254 11 7
£12.99, pp. 130, 2009

In this remarkable book Paul Gordon argues that therapy is a moral endeavour rather than a technical one and spells out the implications of this when working in the consulting room. He questions the idea of frameworks within psychotherapy and counselling, fearing that they restrict space for thought and creativity, and suggests psychotherapy has much to learn from the creative arts such as painting and music, where creativity can only flourish if it is free from external constraints.

This book is an argument for therapeutic freedom at a time when hyper-regulation and state interference threaten to suffocate and dominate psychotherapeutic practice. Therapy is inherently an ethical endeavour, both in the sense that the therapist is called upon to be responsible to and for the other who seeks help, and in the sense that it is inevitably bound up with ideas about how we should live and how we should treat one another.

CONTENTS

PCCS Books   www.pccs-books.co.uk   Tel: +44 (0)1989 763900
2 Cropper Row, Alton Rd, Ross-on-Wye, HR9 5LA

PCCS Books

independent publishing
for independent thinkers

www.pccs-books.co.uk